It is impossible to be a mathematician without being a poet in soul.
-Sophie Kowalevski

Published by Lamberton Press LLC, Evanston, IL.

Senior Editor: Lana Rayckem
Associate Editor: Robert Michael
Editorial Assistant: Katherine Claire
Graphic Design: Gene VanBuren
Cover Design: Stacy Buffham

Plots generated with Python Plotly.
Graphical elements produced with TikZ.
Typeset in LaTeX.

Website: www.mathletters.com
Contact: contact@mathletters.com

ISBN: 978-0-578-28204-6

First Edition

Printed in the United States of America.
10 9 8 7 6 5 4 3 2 1

Table of Contents

Frequently Asked Questions

Why should I read this book?

Broadly speaking, the majority of our readers fall into one or more of the following categories:

High school/college students: Much of the math we learn in school has no direct application to our daily lives, leading to the age-old refrain: "when am I ever going to use this?". But this question misses the point. To use a sports analogy: studying math is like running. Although the end goal may be to play a sport like soccer, football, or basketball, all of them require some form of running. Math is like running, but for your brain.

Any intellectual endeavor you hope to undertake in the future will require some form of creative problem-solving and logical thinking. At its core, mathematics is a pure exercise in these two critical skill sets.

Even if you are inclined to view math as a cold hard science, remember that the subject is not all numbers and formulas. The concept of infinity, the existence of the prime numbers, and the haunting beauty of chaotic systems can inspire artists, philosophers, and poets alike.

Parents: If you already possess an appreciation for mathematics, then this book will help you share that appreciation with your children. On the other hand, if you've never been fond of the subject, this book will showcase a side of mathematics you've probably never seen before. It is much easier to encourage your child to excel in math if you take an interest in the subject yourself.

Students and parents can read this book in tandem. Most of the topics will be new to everyone, and discussing the Collatz conjecture, Buffon's Needle Problem, or uncountable infinity over family dinner is certainly more exciting than discussing the quadratic formula.

Professionals: Business professionals and MBA students focused in sectors where mathematical concepts play a pivotal role, such as finance or technology, will undoubtedly benefit from the ideas in this book.

Retirees: The thrill of learning something new does not dissipate with age. Mathematics is the language of our universe, and many of the ideas in these letters are truly awe-inspiring. There is no better way to keep your brain in shape, and the spark of curiosity alive, than immersing yourself in the world of mathematics.

What mathematical background is required?

There are no formal prerequisites beyond arithmetic. When a new concept is encountered, it will be explained within the context of the letter in which it appears. However, we include a useful review of basic mathematical concepts to refresh your memory before the first letter.

More important than any background in mathematics is a certain level of maturity and patience. Reading about math is not like reading a newspaper or a novel; it is common to reread a sentence or scan a mathematical expression several times before it starts to click.

Why letters?

Math Letters is also available as a bi-weekly letter subscription, and offers a unique way to share the joy of mathematics with friends and family. Subscribers are slowly introduced to new topics as the letters arrive. The goal is to mimic the "drip" style of learning where chunked content is delivered on a schedule. The simple joy of receiving a letter in the mail and reading it at your leisure is a calming antidote to the deluge of information served through digital screens. Visit our website www.mathletters.com to learn more.

Is this a textbook?

No, not in the traditional sense. There are plenty of math books that focus on teaching a particular topic through examples and exercises. In contrast, Math Letters strives to pull back the curtain and offer a glimpse of just how fascinating the field can be. In brief, the purpose of this book is not to teach a particular topic, but to spark your curiosity and present new ways of thinking.

What if I'm no good at math?

There is a prevalent myth, especially in the United States, that some people simply don't "have the brain for math". This belief is generally not true; learning math takes persistence and practice just like anything else. Students do well in the subject if they have the proper encouragement to power through the insecurity caused by confusion. Like most things, hard work is much more important than any perceived natural ability.

That being said, you don't need to be "good" at math to appreciate it—just like you don't have to be a talented artist to appreciate a painting. While each letter will require effort and patience, the ultimate goal is insight and wonder as opposed to computation and memorization.

Review of Basic Mathematical Concepts

In order to read we need to know the alphabet. We then build on this knowledge by learning that different letters can be combined into words, and that words can be combined into sentences. After mastering sentences we intuit the endless possibilities of expression through language. In mathematics, numbers are analogous to the alphabet, and the four basic operations of addition, subtraction, multiplication, and division show us how to combine and manipulate them. Countless shortcuts, properties, and rules arise from combining these operations and can be thought of as the grammar of mathematics. Without a firm understanding of this grammar, reading mathematical expressions can be difficult.

This section is meant as a reference, and you will likely have at least some familiarity with most of the topics. Feel free to skip this review and refer back as needed.

Each of the four basic arithmetic operators are presented along with a traditional computation method you may remember from school. Although efficient, these techniques are not always intuitive, and can lead to rote memorization instead of insight. This review will attempt to briefly demystify each traditional method and, when possible, show an alternative. We then discuss how the various operators interact and combine. Higher mathematics has much more to do with patterns and abstract reasoning than it does with calculation, so knowing how to quickly calculate using pencil and paper is less important than knowing the algebraic rules the numbers abide by.

Counting and the Integers

Counting is the most basic mathematical idea, and the first math concept most children learn. Our fingers act as a nice visual device when counting up to 10. The digits 0-9 offer a convenient way to express quantities without holding up fingers. Many arithmetic operations can be thought of as clever time-saving devices to avoid the arduous task of counting.

The fact that we have 10 fingers is why our number system is based on multiples of 10. For instance, the number 3256 is actually 3 1000s, 2 100s, 5 10s, and 6 1s. This is the origin of the term "place" when referring to the digits in a number. The 3 is in the 1000s place, the 2 is in the 100s place, and so on.

The term *integer* refers to our usual counting numbers 1, 2, 3, 4, ... which are sometimes referred to as *whole numbers*. Technically, the integers contain 0 and all the negative whole numbers as well.

Addition

Addition is an efficient method of computing the total without having to count each object individually. If one person has 7 apples and another has 5 apples, we don't need to dump them in a pile and start counting to determine that there are 12 apples in total. The rules of addition simplify this to $5 + 7 = 12$.

There is some memorization when first learning addition, but the bulk of the work lies in memorizing the sum of all combinations of the digits 0-9.

Adding large numbers is typically taught using the "carry" method in grade school:

$$\begin{array}{r} \overset{1}{2}82 \\ + \ 137 \\ \hline 419 \end{array}$$

A number is carried to the next column whenever the sum of a column equals 10 or more. For instance, a 1 is carried from the middle column to the leftmost column because the result of adding 8 and 3 is 11. This happens because $80 + 30 = 110$, so a 1 is written in the 10s place of the answer to account for the 10 in 110. The remaining 100 is added to the 100s place by "carrying the 1" into the next column.

There is an alternative to the carry method for computing sums. First, break each number down into multiples of 100s, 10s, and 1s:

$$282 + 137 = (200 + 80 + 2) + (100 + 30 + 7)$$

Then group the 100s, 10s, and 1s. Each of the 3 sums in parentheses are easy because they only involve 2 nonzero digits:

$$(200 + 100) + (80 + 30) + (2 + 7)$$

Perform the addition in each parentheses and sum them up from left to right:

$$300 + 110 + 9 = 419$$

Any integer can be broken apart into its respective 1s, 10s, 100s, 1000s, etc. places by using addition. For example:

$$3256 = 3000 + 200 + 50 + 6$$

This is a useful trick to remember.

In most math books outside of grade school, addition and subtraction will usually be written horizontally:

$$282 + 137$$

Notice that the terms in a sum can be freely rearranged:

$$282 + 137 = 137 + 282 = 419$$

Subtraction

Subtraction is the inverse of addition. That is, if you add one number to another, you can undo the addition using subtraction. You see this a lot in mathematics—one operation acting as the inverse of another.

Subtraction is traditionally taught using the "borrow" method in school:

$$\begin{array}{r} \overset{7\,1}{2\cancel{8}2} \\ -\ 137 \\ \hline 145 \end{array}$$

This is analogous to the "carry" method of addition, but in reverse. Unfortunately, it is much less intuitive. Even adults will have a hard time explaining exactly why this method works. It gets even more complicated when you need to borrow across multiple columns. Sadly, this is where many young students start to view math as a collection of memorizations, and it's hard to blame them.

The subtraction in the right column, or 1s place, is $2 - 7 = -5$. This is not good, because the final answer can't have a negative number in the 1s place—that wouldn't make any sense.

To arrive at a number that does make sense, the borrowing technique steals multiples of 10 from the next column over to correct for the negative value. The first subtraction of $2 - 7$ results in a negative number, so move one column to the left and "borrow" a 10 from the 8 in the 10s place of 282. Add this 10 to the 2 to get 12. This is the origin of the $12 - 7$ subtraction in the right column. The borrowed 10 turns the 8 into a 7 in the middle column.

If the borrow method brings back bad memories, you are not alone. It lives on because it *is* a very efficient way to perform subtraction with pencil and paper.

Like addition, there is an alternative way to do subtraction by hand. First, break apart each number into multiples of 100s, 10s, and 1s:

$$282 = 200 + 80 + 2$$
$$137 = 100 + 30 + 7$$

Now write out the subtraction using these forms of the numbers:

$$200 + 80 + 2 - 100 - 30 - 7$$

Group the 100s, 10s, and 1s together:

$$(200 - 100) + (80 - 30) + (2 - 7)$$

Each of these 3 subtractions are easy because they only involve 2 nonzero digits. Finally, perform each subtraction and add up the results.

$$100 + 50 + -5 = 145$$

This method involves a bit more writing, but it is much more intuitive and there is no borrowing.

Note that adding a positive number to a negative number is the same as subtraction—in other words:

$$50 + -5 = 50 - 5 = 45$$

Unlike addition, the terms in a subtraction cannot be rearranged:

$$5 - 3 \neq 3 - 5$$

However, there is a simple trick that can be used to write any subtraction as an addition if we want to rearrange the terms: write the subtraction as an addition using a negative number.

$$5 - 3 = 5 + (-3)$$

Now this sum can be freely rearranged:

$$5 + (-3) = (-3) + 5 = 2$$

Multiplication

For integers, multiplication is a shorthand way to add many copies of the same number together. Instead of writing $7 + 7 + 7 + 7$ it is much easier to write $4 \cdot 7$. The result of a multiplication is called the *product*. Sometimes multiplication is written using the $\times$ symbol, but in more advanced math books this symbol is easily confused with the variable x, so the dot notation $\cdot$ is the preferred choice.

Although we will usually write the multiplication dot in this book, it is not uncommon to omitted it entirely, particularly when expressions in parentheses are involved:

$$2 \cdot (3 + 4) = 2(3 + 4)$$

Or when variables and symbols like square roots appear:

$$7 \cdot y \cdot \sqrt{2} = 7y\sqrt{2}$$

Like addition, the terms in a multiplication can be rearranged without affecting the answer:

$$56 \cdot 27 = 27 \cdot 56 = 1512$$

Traditional multiplication by hand looks like this:

$$
\begin{array}{r}
56 \\
\times\ 27 \\
\hline
392 \\
+1120 \\
\hline
1512
\end{array}
$$

Digits are cross multiplied together one by one and several "carries" are involved, similar to the "carry" routine in traditional addition. The carries are not shown here because it starts to look even more confusing than it already is. Like the borrow method of subtraction, this technique is efficient for multiplying by hand, but it is certainly not intuitive.

The traditional method works by completing several easier multiplications and adding them together. To explore the origin of this technique we will first break apart each number into its 10s and 1s place:

$$56 = 50 + 6$$
$$27 = 20 + 7$$

Now multiply these together:

$$(50 + 6) \cdot (20 + 7)$$

Writing multiplication horizontally using the dot notation is how it will usually be displayed in advanced math books.

The distributive property of multiplication can be applied to write this product as:

$$(50 + 6) \cdot (20 + 7) = 50 \cdot 20 + 50 \cdot 7 + 6 \cdot 20 + 6 \cdot 7$$

If you are confused by the equality above don't worry, we will discuss the distributive property later in this review. The four products $50 \cdot 20$, $50 \cdot 7$, $6 \cdot 20$, and $6 \cdot 7$ are the easier multiplications performed when using the traditional method.

Now compute the four multiplications to get:

$$1000 + 350 + 120 + 42$$

The 350 and 42 combine to make 392 and the 1000 and 120 combine to make 1120. This explains the final addition in the traditional method:

$$
\begin{array}{r}
392 \\
+1120 \\
\hline
1512
\end{array}
$$

Computing multiplications is more difficult than addition or subtraction both on paper and in your head. That's because multiplication of integers is the same as repeated addition, so multiplying 56 by 27 is like adding 27 copies of 56 together, or 56 copies of 27 together.

An alternative approach for pencil and paper multiplication is the "box method". It mimics exactly what we did above for multiplying $56 \cdot 27 = (50 + 6) \cdot (20 + 7)$ but organizes it in a more visually pleasing way.

First, draw a 2 by 2 box containing 4 cells. Along one edge (it doesn't matter which one) write the 50 and the 6, and along the other write the 20 and the 7:

In each box multiply the number on the left with the number on the top:

	20	7
50	1000	350
6	120	42

For the final answer sum all the boxes together:

$$
\begin{array}{r}
1000 \\
350 \\
120 \\
+42 \\
\hline
1512
\end{array}
$$

This technique works for numbers of any length as long as the boxes are drawn accordingly. Here is the setup for $123 \cdot 45$:

	100	20	3
40			
5			

Computing multiplications by hand is an impressive skill to have, but a calculator will also suffice.

Division

Division is the inverse of multiplication. For example, notice how the division by 4 cancels the multiplication by 4, leaving only 3:

$$
\frac{3 \cdot 4}{4} = 3
$$

Like the multiplication symbol $\times$, the division symbol $\div$ is not used in advanced math. Writing divisions as one number over another is the preferred method, as in $\frac{12}{4}$ to divide 12 by 4. The 4 in $\frac{12}{4}$ is called the *divisor*, and the answer to this division is 3 since 3 4s go into 12.

There is a third symbol associated with division—the long division symbol. Long division is a traditional manual computation method and usually looks like this:

$$
\begin{array}{r}
128 \\
2\,)\overline{256} \\
-200 \\
\hline
56 \\
-40 \\
\hline
16
\end{array}
$$

At least long division works from left to right, unlike other traditional methods. The number 128 written on top is how many times 2 goes into 256.

Long division uses a trick to speed up the process of finding the answer. Instead of trying to divide 256 by 2 directly, it starts with multiples of 100 times 2, then multiples of 10 times 2, and finally multiples of 1 times 2.

The 1 in the hundreds place of 128 is found by noticing that 100 2s go into 256. Now 100 2s is only equal to 200, so we still need to find how many 2s go into the remaining quantity $256 - 200 = 56$. This explains the subtraction of 200 below 256.

The 2 in the tens place of 128 is found by noticing that 20 2s go into 56; however, 20 2s is only equal to 40, so we still need to find how many 2s go into the remaining quantity $56 - 40 = 16$. This explains the subtraction of 40 below 56.

Finally, 8 2s go into 16, the last remaining quantity. This gives the final 8 in the ones place of 128.

The division operator spawns a new class of numbers known as the *rational* numbers that are formed by dividing one integer by another. The number on top is called the *numerator* and the number on the bottom is the *denominator*. We will have more to say about rational numbers later in this review, but they occur because most integers do not divide evenly into one another. For instance, dividing 89 by 4 leaves a remainder of 1. This is due to the fact that only 22 4s can go into 89 without going over. Sometimes the remainder is written with a little "r" in long division:

$$
\begin{array}{r}
22 \quad r1 \\
4\,\overline{)\,89} \\
-88 \\
\hline
1
\end{array}
$$

On a calculator, divisions with remainders will manifest as numbers to the right of the decimal point:

$$\frac{89}{4} = 22.25$$

In most math texts, though, the division of $\frac{89}{4}$ is left as is and viewed as just another number.

The most important point to remember about division is that it is the inverse of multiplication. Given a division such as:

$$\frac{243}{786}$$

the divisor of 786 is canceled if we multiply by 786, leaving only the numerator of 243:

$$786 \cdot \frac{243}{786} = 243$$

Exponents

Just as multiplication is a shorthand way to sum many copies of the same number together, exponents are a shorthand way to multiply many copies of the same number together. Instead of writing $5 \cdot 5 \cdot 5 \cdot 5$ it is much easier to write 5^4. The 5 is called the *base* and the 4 is known as the *power* or *exponent*. The expression 5^4 is usually read as "five raised to the fourth power" or "five with an exponent of four". The most familiar numbers with exponents are squared numbers such as $3^2 = 3 \cdot 3 = 9$.

Square Roots

As mentioned above, the most familiar exponent is 2. Squared numbers and variables arise in many settings, and high school textbooks are filled with equations like $x^2 + 5x - 3$. Suppose we want to solve this simple equation:

$$x^2 = 25$$

The solution x will be a number such that when squared yields 25. This type of situation is so common that mathematicians came up with a symbol to represent the inverse of squaring; it is known as the square root. The square root of 25 is written as:

$$\sqrt{25} = 5$$

There is one thing we must mention about square roots. If we restrict to the positive numbers, every number has 1 square root. However, if we allow for negative numbers, then each number has two square roots. That's because multiplying two negative numbers yields a positive, so $5 \cdot 5 = 25$, but it is also true that $(-5) \cdot (-5) = 25$. Both 5 and -5 are equal to $\sqrt{25}$. In this book, we will usually be concerned with the positive square root.

Taking the square root of a square number like $6^2 = 36$ results in an integer $\sqrt{36} = 6$, but this is a special case—usually the result will be a never-ending decimal number like $\sqrt{7} = 2.6457....$ When used in equations, most square roots are not converted to decimals since attempting to write them out is futile.

Variables

Mathematics thrives on abstraction. It is much more powerful to prove a general result than it is to prove a specific calculation. If a right triangle has sides of length 3 and 4, then measuring the hypotenuse shows that it has length $\sqrt{3^2 + 4^2} = \sqrt{25} = 5$. This relationship between the sides and the hypotenuse only represents one specific triangle.

The idea that *any* right triangle with side lengths a and b must have $\sqrt{a^2 + b^2}$ as its hypotenuse is much more powerful, because it applies to every right triangle.

The basic tool mathematicians use to propose and prove general theorems is the variable. A variable is simply a placeholder for a number. It frees us from having to work with specific numbers. Applying arithmetic operations to variables is no different than applying them to numbers.

The letter n is generally used to stand in for integers, and the letters x and y are traditionally used to stand in for decimal numbers. The letters a, b, and c also appear frequently. The actual choice of letter is inconsequential and usually dictated by nothing more than tradition.

As mentioned earlier, it is common to leave off the multiplication dot when multiplying numbers with variables. The expression:

$$2x + 7y - 5 \cdot 8$$

could be written more verbosely as:

$$2 \cdot x + 7 \cdot y - 5 \cdot 8$$

Arithmetic works the same on variables as it does on numbers. Adding 3 copies of x to 2 copies of y gives:

$$x + x + x + y + y = 3x + 2y$$

Dividing $2x$ by $3x$ will cancel x just as if it were a number:

$$\frac{2x}{3x} = \frac{2}{3}$$

Adding $2yx$ to $4xy$ gives $6xy$ because the order of multiplication $yx = xy$ doesn't matter:

$$2yx + 4xy = 6xy$$

Expressions can sometimes appear overwhelming when many variables are involved, but never forget that they are just placeholders for numbers.

Distributive Property of Multiplication

When the different arithmetic operations begin to intermix there are certain rules that naturally arise. The distributive property is one of them, and it is extremely important. It represents the outcome of mixing multiplication with addition. Given numbers a, b, and c the property states:

$$a \cdot (b + c) = a \cdot b + a \cdot c$$

Here is an example using the numbers 2, 3, and 4 to stand in for a, b, and c.

$$2 \cdot (3 + 4) = 2 \cdot 3 + 2 \cdot 4$$

To see why the distributive property is true, recall that multiplication is shorthand for adding many copies of the same number (in this case, 2 copies of the number $(3+4)$). Don't let the $(3 + 4)$ term confuse you. It is just a number like any other, but instead of adding to get 7 we will leave the sum as it is:

$$2 \cdot (3 + 4) = (3 + 4) + (3 + 4)$$

The order of addition does not matter, so the sum on the right can be rearranged to group the 3s and 4s together:

$$2 \cdot (3 + 4) = (3 + 4) + (3 + 4)$$
$$= 3 + 3 + 4 + 4$$

Adding two copies of 3 is the same as $2 \cdot 3$ and adding two copies of 4 is the same as $2 \cdot 4$:

$$2 \cdot (3 + 4) = (3 + 4) + (3 + 4)$$
$$= 3 + 3 + 4 + 4$$
$$= 2 \cdot 3 + 2 \cdot 4$$

We've arrived at the distributive property of multiplication.

It works across a sum or subtraction of any length:

$$5 \cdot (3 + 4 - 5) = 5 \cdot 3 + 5 \cdot 4 - 5 \cdot 5$$

The distributive property is sometimes used in reverse to "pull out a common factor". For instance, in the sum:
$$2 \cdot 3 + 2 \cdot 4$$
each term has a multiplication factor of 2. It can be pulled out and rewritten as:

$$2 \cdot 3 + 2 \cdot 4 = 2 \cdot (3 + 4)$$

FOIL

FOIL is an acronym for First, Outer, Inner, Last. It's a way to remember the order of multiplication when multiplying two sums. The rule is usually expressed as:

$$(a + b) \cdot (c + d) = a \cdot c + a \cdot d + b \cdot c + b \cdot d$$

The $a \cdot c$ term is composed of the "first" variable in each parentheses, the $a \cdot d$ term consists of the "outer" variable in each parentheses, and so on.

The FOIL method is really just a few applications of the distributive property of multiplication in disguise. To see why, recall the distributive property example from above:

$$2 \cdot (3 + 4) = 2 \cdot 3 + 2 \cdot 4$$

Think of the 2 as $(a + b)$, the 3 as c, and the 4 as d. Now distribute the $(a + b)$ over c and d:

$$(a + b) \cdot (c + d) = (a + b) \cdot c + (a + b) \cdot d$$

It might take a moment to see what is happening. The only difference here is that we're using abstract quantities like $(a + b)$ instead of numbers like 2. Now apply the distributive property two more times, once for $(a + b) \cdot c$ and once for $(a + b) \cdot d$:

$$(a + b) \cdot (c + d) = (a + b) \cdot c + (a + b) \cdot d$$
$$= a \cdot c + b \cdot c + (a + b) \cdot d$$
$$= a \cdot c + b \cdot c + a \cdot d + b \cdot d$$
$$= a \cdot c + a \cdot d + b \cdot c + b \cdot d$$

The last line just rearranges the terms to line up with FOIL.

The FOIL method was used to arrive at this equality in the earlier section on multiplication:

$$(50 + 6) \cdot (20 + 7) = 50 \cdot 20 + 50 \cdot 7 + 6 \cdot 20 + 6 \cdot 7$$

Why teach FOIL if it is just the distributive property of multiplication? Multiplying sums together arises quite often, and rather than apply the distributive property step by step, we can take a shortcut and memorize the FOIL rule. This is the case for many seemingly mysterious mathematical formulas; they are actually just shortcuts to save time.

Here is another formula:

$$(a + b)^2 = a^2 + 2 \cdot a \cdot b + b^2$$

It might look complicated at first glance, but this is another example of the FOIL method where $(c + d)$ has been replaced with another copy of $(a + b)$. This is easy to see if we recall that:

$$(a + b)^2 = (a + b) \cdot (a + b)$$

Order of Operations (PEMDAS)

PEMDAS is an acronym for Parentheses, Exponents, Multiplication, Division, Addition, Subtraction. It's a way to remember the order of operations when they are mixed together. Using this expression:

$$2 \cdot 3^2 + 7 - 4 + \frac{8 \cdot (9 + 1)}{10}$$

first compute anything in parentheses. In this case $(9 + 1)$:

$$2 \cdot 3^2 + 7 - 4 + \frac{8 \cdot 10}{10}$$

Now compute exponents, so $3^2 = 9$:

$$2 \cdot 9 + 7 - 4 + \frac{8 \cdot 10}{10}$$

Then do the multiplications $2 \cdot 9 = 18$ and $8 \cdot 10 = 80$:

$$18 + 7 - 4 + \frac{80}{10}$$

Division is next:

$$18 + 7 - 4 + 8$$

Finally, compute the addition and subtraction:

$$18 + 7 - 4 + 8 = 29$$

The order of operations ensures that everyone arrives at the same answer no matter how complicated the expression. There is some reasoning behind the convention. Operations that are built upon others are applied first. For instance, exponents are a form of multiplication, and multiplication is a form of addition. PEMDAS works its way down to the simplest operations of addition and subtraction.

PEMDAS can lead to a great deal of confusion when expressions are written using the traditional division symbol $\div$ instead of the fraction bar:

$$6 \div 2 \cdot 4$$

Which comes first: the division $6 \div 2$ or the multiplication $2 \cdot 4$? The "M" comes before the "D" in PEMDAS, so you'd probably think that $2 \cdot 4 = 8$ should be executed first. Unfortunately, the acronym doesn't include a critical piece of information for this type of situation. When applying multiplication and division at the same time, execute it *from left to right*. In this case, $6 \div 2$ comes first, and it should be performed before the multiplication:

$$6 \div 2 \cdot 4 = 3 \cdot 4 = 12$$

This is yet another reason why the $\div$ symbol is not used outside of grade school. Using the fraction bar, this expression would be written as:

$$\frac{6}{2} \cdot 4$$

Now it is clear that 2 is a divisor, and there is little chance of mistakingly multiplying the 2 and the 4.

Parentheses are a bit like punctuation in writing. They are used to make formulas easier to read, but they are also used to change the order of operations. The expression:

$$2 \cdot 3 + 4$$

would normally be computed as:

$$6 + 4 = 10$$

However, if $3 + 4$ should be computed first, just add parentheses:

$$2 \cdot (3 + 4)$$

This changes the meaning of the expression because anything in parentheses is always done first. Now it is equal to:

$$2 \cdot 7 = 14$$

Applying Operations to Both Sides of an Equation

Equations are ubiquitous in mathematics, and they generally express an equality. For instance:

$$(2 + 5) = 7$$

The two sides of the expression above are equal to one another. This means that as long as the *same* basic arithmetic operation is applied to *both* sides of the equation, it will remain valid. We could multiply both sides by 3:

$$3 \cdot (2 + 5) = 3 \cdot 7$$

and divide both sides by 10:

$$\frac{3 \cdot (2 + 5)}{10} = \frac{3 \cdot 7}{10}$$

and add 6 to both sides:

$$6 + \frac{3 \cdot (2 + 5)}{10} = 6 + \frac{3 \cdot 7}{10}$$

The point is that as long as the first equation is true, all of the following equations are true. Importantly, this works the other way as well, as long as the last equation is true, the first equation is true.

Applying an operation to only one side of an equality, or applying a different operation to each side, would invalidate it. This should be intuitively obvious. We can't simply multiply the left side by 2 and the right side by 3:

$$2 \cdot (2 + 5) = 3 \cdot 7$$

This would imply that $14 = 21$, which is silly. The equality breaks if the same operation isn't applied to both sides.

Of course, it is far more common to see equations involving variables:

$$\frac{9x - 6}{2} = 3x$$

Usually, the goal is to find the number x that makes the expression true. To do this, x must be isolated on one side, and the basic tools at our disposal are addition, subtraction, multiplication, and division. The only thing to remember is that the same operation must always be applied to both sides.

Let's start by multiplying both sides by 2:

$$2 \cdot \frac{9x - 6}{2} = 2 \cdot 3x$$

This will cancel the 2 in the denominator on the left:

$$9x - 6 = 2 \cdot 3x$$

Now subtract $2 \cdot 3x$ from both sides.

$$9x - 6 - 2 \cdot 3x = 2 \cdot 3x - 2 \cdot 3x$$

This will leave 0 on the right side since $2 \cdot 3x - 2 \cdot 3x = 0$:

$$9x - 6 - 2 \cdot 3x = 0$$

Add 6 to both sides:

$$9x - 6 - 2 \cdot 3x + 6 = 6$$

The 6 on the left will disappear because $-6 + 6 = 0$:

$$9x - 2 \cdot 3x = 6$$

The left side can be simplified to $9x - 2 \cdot 3x = 9x - 6x = 3x$ to get:

$$3x = 6$$

Finally, divide both sides by 3 to isolate x on the left side:

$$x = \frac{6}{3}$$

The solution is $x = \frac{6}{3}$ or $x = 2$.

Knowing exactly which operations to apply, and in which order, is often more of an art than a science. It takes practice just like anything else.

Quadratic Formula

The quadratic formula is a mainstay of middle school math. It applies to situations where both an x term *and* an x^2 term are involved:

$$2x^2 - 10x + 12 = 0$$

Finding solutions to this equation requires a series of tedious operations, and it is much easier to memorize a formula. Known as the *quadratic formula*, the solutions for x are given by:

$$x = \frac{-b \pm \sqrt{b^2 - 4ac}}{2a}$$

The variables a and b correspond to the coefficients, or multipliers, of the x^2 and x terms respectively. In this case $a = 2$ and $b = -10$. The last variable c corresponds to the last term in the equation, which is 12. The "$\pm$" signifies that there are actually two solutions for x. One of them is found by taking the negative square root, and the other using the positive square root.

For example, one solution is obtained by replacing the $\pm$ with $+$ for the positive square root and plugging in for a, b, and c:

$$x = \frac{10 + \sqrt{(-10)^2 - 4 \cdot 2 \cdot 12}}{2 \cdot 2} = 3$$

The other solution is found by taking the negative square root:

$$x = \frac{10 - \sqrt{(-10)^2 - 4 \cdot 2 \cdot 12}}{2 \cdot 2} = 2$$

We can check that both solutions work. Replacing x with 3 gives:

$$2 \cdot 3^2 - 10 \cdot 3 + 12 = 18 - 30 + 12 = 0$$

And replacing x with 2 gives:

$$2 \cdot 2^2 - 10 \cdot 2 + 12 = 8 - 20 + 12 = 0$$

So both solutions are indeed correct. In short, the quadratic formula is a mechanical way to quickly arrive at solutions for equations of the form:

$$ax^2 + bx + c = 0$$

Fractions

So far only the integers, sometimes referred to as whole numbers, have been used in our examples—but all of the arithmetic operations can be applied to ratios of integers, or what mathematicians call *rational* numbers. In everyday language, the term *fraction* is often used to describe these numbers.

Fractions are generally written in their ratio form as opposed to their decimal form. This is because it is easier to work with ratios when performing manual calculations. Imagine having to write $0.42857142857...$ over and over instead of $\frac{3}{7}$ when using pencil and paper. Nonetheless, it is sometimes more natural to use the decimal form, and both ratios and decimals will be used in this book.

From a mathematical standpoint, fractions represent nothing more than the division of one integer by another. However, a more practical viewpoint is to think of fractions as quantities denoted in units other than 1. For example, the fraction $\frac{3}{4}$ represents 3 units of $\frac{1}{4}$, the fraction $\frac{5}{8}$ represents 5 units of $\frac{1}{8}$, and so on. This system should be familiar to anyone who has ever used a tape measure. A measurement of ten and three-eighths of an inch represents 10 whole units of 1 inch and 3 units of $\frac{1}{8}$ inch.

Multiplying fractions is straightforward. The numerators and denominators multiply together:

$$\frac{2}{7} \cdot \frac{3}{8} = \frac{2 \cdot 3}{7 \cdot 8} = \frac{6}{56}$$

When fractions are raised to a power, parentheses are used to make it clear that the power applies to the entire fraction:

$$\left(\frac{1}{2}\right)^2 = \frac{1}{2} \cdot \frac{1}{2} = \frac{1}{4}$$

Adding and dividing fractions is a bit more complicated. The main reason for this is that forming a fraction is essentially dividing one number by another. Therefore, adding fractions mixes division with addition, and dividing fractions is akin to performing multiple divisions at the same time.

The key to working with fractions is to realize that the actual quantity the fraction represents *does not change if the numerator and denominator are multiplied by the same number*. For example, we can multiply the fraction $\frac{1}{2}$ by $\frac{2}{2}$ to get:

$$\frac{2}{2} \cdot \frac{1}{2} = \frac{2}{4}$$

Both $\frac{1}{2}$ and $\frac{2}{4}$ are equal to .5. Any number over itself is equal to 1, so all we're doing is multiplying by a specific representation of 1 like $\frac{2}{2}$. Likewise, we could multiply $\frac{1}{2}$ by $\frac{3}{3}$ or any other number over itself without altering the quantity.

How can we use this knowledge to add two fractions? Unfortunately, we cannot simply add the numerators and denominators:

$$\frac{2}{7} + \frac{3}{8} \neq \frac{2+3}{7+8}$$

One way to understand this is to observe that we are trying to add two different *units* together. If we wanted to add $\frac{2}{7}$ths of an inch to $\frac{3}{8}$ths of an inch we would first need to convert to a common unit—and that's what we'll do here.

The goal is to make the denominators equal, or in other words, write each fraction using the same units. This is where the trick of multiplying each fraction by a number over itself comes in handy.

Multiply the first term by $\frac{8}{8}$ and the second term by $\frac{7}{7}$:

$$\frac{8}{8} \cdot \frac{2}{7} + \frac{7}{7} \cdot \frac{3}{8}$$

Remember, this doesn't change the problem because $\frac{8}{8} = 1$ and $\frac{7}{7} = 1$.

Performing the multiplication yields:

$$\frac{8 \cdot 2}{8 \cdot 7} + \frac{7 \cdot 3}{7 \cdot 8} = \frac{16}{56} + \frac{21}{56}$$

The $\frac{8}{8}$ and $\frac{7}{7}$ were chosen so that both denominators come out to the same number: 56. Now that each term is expressed in the same units, the numerators can be summed to yield the answer:

$$\frac{16}{56} + \frac{21}{56} = \frac{16+21}{56} = \frac{37}{56}$$

To ensure that this is correct, you can try adding $\frac{2}{7}$ and $\frac{3}{8}$ on a calculator. The answer will be precisely the same as $\frac{37}{56}$ when written as a decimal.

In summary, to add fractions there must be a common unit (in school this is often referred to as "finding a common denominator").

There is a rule you can memorize to quickly add fractions, and the sequence of steps above is the story behind why it works:

$$\frac{2 \hspace{0.5em} 3}{7 \hspace{0.5em} 8} = \frac{2 \cdot 8 + 7 \cdot 3}{7 \cdot 8} = \frac{37}{56}$$

The cross products $2 \cdot 8$ and $7 \cdot 3$ are summed in the numerator, and the common denominator is found by multiplying the two denominators 7 and 8.

Let's move on to dividing fractions. Since each fraction itself represents a division, there are multiple divisions mixed together:

$$\frac{\left(\frac{2}{7}\right)}{\left(\frac{3}{8}\right)}$$

Our goal is to simplify the expression into a single fraction of one integer over another. To accomplish this, we will use the same trick of multiplying by various carefully chosen representations of 1.

First, multiply by $\frac{8}{8}$:

$$\frac{8}{8} \cdot \frac{\left(\frac{2}{7}\right)}{\left(\frac{3}{8}\right)}$$

This is just like multiplying two fractions together, so one of the 8s multiplies the numerator and the other one multiplies the denominator:

$$\frac{8 \cdot \left(\frac{2}{7}\right)}{8 \cdot \left(\frac{3}{8}\right)}$$

In the denominator the 8s cancel leaving only 3:

$$\frac{8 \cdot \left(\frac{2}{7}\right)}{3}$$

Now multiply by $\frac{7}{7}$:

$$\frac{7}{7} \cdot \frac{8 \cdot \left(\frac{2}{7}\right)}{3}$$

Again, the top 7 multiplies the numerator and the bottom 7 multiplies the denominator:

$$\frac{7 \cdot 8 \cdot \left(\frac{2}{7}\right)}{7 \cdot 3}$$

Now the 7s in the numerator cancel leaving only $8 \cdot 2$:

$$\frac{8 \cdot 2}{7 \cdot 3}$$

We've arrived at the final simplified answer:

$$\frac{8 \cdot 2}{7 \cdot 3} = \frac{16}{21}$$

The calculations above are the origin of the "cross multiplying" rule for dividing fractions, which is another rule that wraps all the steps we just completed into an easy formula. For visual reasons, it is usually written using the $\div$ symbol instead of the fraction bar:

$$\frac{2}{7} \div \frac{3}{8} = \frac{2 \cdot 8}{7 \cdot 3} = \frac{16}{21}$$

The numerator of the first term and denominator of the second term multiply to get the new numerator $2 \cdot 8$. Then the denominator of the first term and numerator of the second term multiply to get the new denominator $7 \cdot 3$.

Mixed fractions, sometimes called mixed numbers, like $4\frac{5}{8}$ are rarely seen in math books beyond grade school. Instead, these will always be written as improper fractions:

$$4\frac{5}{8} = \frac{37}{8}$$

The term "improper fraction" is a name given to fractions where the numerator is larger than the denominator. The division $\frac{37}{8}$ is equal to 4.625; the same as 4 plus $\frac{5}{8}$.

Functions

The idea behind functions is meant to be rather simple: a function takes in one or more numbers, applies some operations, and produces an output. Functions are always written using variables because they can usually accept any number. The function to square a number is:

$$x^2$$

The function to square a number and add 5 is:

$$x^2 + 5$$

The result of the function above with an input of $x = 2$ is:

$$2^2 + 5 = 4 + 5 = 9$$

Sometimes functions are written using the $f(x)$ notation. The f stands for "function".

$$f(x) = x^2 + 5$$

This notation makes it easy to see what number is being plugged in for x:

$$f(2) = 2^2 + 5 = 9$$

A function doesn't have to accept a single input. Here is a function that accepts two inputs:

$$f(x, y) = xy + x - y$$

Plugging in $x = 2$ and $y = 3$ gives:

$$f(2, 3) = 2 \cdot 3 + 2 - 3 = 5$$

Functions are the ideal way to express motion and change, and this is the main source of their popularity. If a car travels at a constant 60 miles per hour on a straight road, then a function that represents the distance traveled in terms of time x is:

$$f(x) = 60x$$

After 5 hours the car will have traveled a distance of $f(5) = 60 \cdot 5 = 300$ miles.

This is a trivial example, but functions are used to model a wide variety of phenomena, from the movement of planets around the sun to the growth of money in a bank account.

Ellipses "..."

The three dots "..." are used in mathematics much like "etc." in writing. Depending on the context, they usually imply the continuation of something.

The continuation of a pattern is one common scenario:

$$1 + 2 + 3 + \ldots + 100$$

The "..." stands in for the numbers between 3 and 100, because it would be too much work to write them all out. Another example:

$$1.345345\ldots$$

In this case, the dots imply the infinite continuation of the trailing decimal pattern 345. If there is no obvious pattern as in 1.294837... then the dots imply an infinite sequence of numbers after the decimal point with no apparent pattern.

Here is one last example:

$$\left(\frac{1}{2}\right)^1 + \left(\frac{1}{2}\right)^2 + \left(\frac{1}{2}\right)^3 + \ldots$$

The pattern should be apparent; each term is a power of $\frac{1}{2}$ and the power increases by 1 per term. The dots imply that this pattern continues forever—an infinite sum.

Admittedly, the three dots are considered a somewhat informal notation in mathematics. However, they are very versatile, and we will use them throughout this book.

Numbers, Integers, Positive Integers, Rational Numbers, and Fractions

Mathematics is a precise science, and so it requires precise language. This often leads to awkward repetition when writing about math. Several topics will deal solely with the positive integers, but repeating the phrase "positive integer" numerous times makes for clunky reading. Therefore, when the context is clear, we will use the term "positive integer" interchangeably with the more colloquial "integer" or simply "number".

The informal term "fraction" will also sometimes be used in place of the more precise mathematical term "rational number" when speaking of ratios of integers.

The Collatz Conjecture

Letter 1

The essence of mathematics lies in its freedom.
-George Cantor

Like many fields of science, the forefront of mathematics has become more esoteric over time. Without specializing in a particular niche, even a trained mathematician will find it difficult to comprehend many of the open questions. That's why it may come as a surprise that one of the most famous unsolved problems in mathematics can be understood by a grade-schooler. The problem statement only involves simple arithmetic and two rules. The rules are given below:

1. If the number is even, divide it by 2.
2. If the number is odd, multiply by 3 and add 1.

The famous *Collatz conjecture*, first proposed by the German mathematician Lothar Collatz in 1937, states that no matter which positive integer is chosen, if the two rules above are applied repeatedly, the sequence of numbers will *always* terminate at the number 1.

Let's pick a positive integer, say 5, and test the conjecture. The number 5 is odd, so apply the second rule which tells us to multiply by 3 and add 1:

$$3 \cdot 5 + 1 = 16$$

Now take this new number 16, and apply the rules again. It is even, so the first rule instructs us to divide by 2 to get 8. Since 8 is even, another application of the rules gives $\frac{8}{2} = 4$. Again 4 is even, so divide to get $\frac{4}{2} = 2$. One last application of the rules (since 2 is even) gives $\frac{2}{2} = 1$. Beginning with the number 5, the sequence generated by repeatedly applying the rules is:

$$5, 16, 8, 4, 2, 1$$

Let's try another number; this time we'll use 13. It is odd, so multiply by 3 and add 1 to get $3 \cdot 13 + 1 = 40$. The new number 40 is even, so divide by 2 to get $\frac{40}{2} = 20$. If we continue on as before, always applying the rules to the new number, the sequence below is generated:

$$13, 40, 20, 10, 5, 16, 8, 4, 2, 1$$

Again, the sequence eventually reaches 1. If we keep going once we reach 1, the sequence cycles back to 1 after a few steps: 1 is odd, so $3 \cdot 1 + 1 = 4$, 4 is even so $\frac{4}{2} = 2$, 2 is even so $\frac{2}{2} = 1$. It is no use trying to escape from 1 once we hit it.

Take a moment to appreciate both the simplicity and the generality of the Collatz conjecture. It claims that no matter which integer is chosen—be it 198, 1254398128, or some massive integer several billions of digits in length—as long as the rules are faithfully applied, the sequence will always reach 1.

There are other famous procedures that, when applied repeatedly, eventually pull any starting number to a single point. The Indian mathematician D.R. Kaprekar discovered one bizarre example in the late 1940s. Start by choosing any four-digit number where at least two of the digits are different. For instance, you cannot choose 1111, but you could choose 1112. Now take this number and apply the following three steps over and over:

1. Arrange the digits in descending order.
2. Take the newly sorted number from step 1 and write it in reverse.
3. Subtract the number in step 2 from the number in step 1.

Let's try it out using the number 8190. Arrange the digits in descending order, 9810, and then reverse it to get 0189. Next, subtract the two numbers:

$$
\begin{array}{r}
9810 \\
- \ 0189 \\
\hline
9621
\end{array}
$$

Notice that 0 is arranged just like any other digit, even though it is redundant in the second number $0189 = 189$. Now let's take 9621 and apply the rules again. The digits already happen to be in descending order, so subtract the number formed by reversing the digits:

$$
\begin{array}{r}
9621 \\
- \ 1269 \\
\hline
8352
\end{array}
$$

Organizing the digits of 8352 into descending order gives 8532. Subtracting the reverse, 2358, yields:

$$
\begin{array}{r}
8532 \\
- \ 2358 \\
\hline
6174
\end{array}
$$

Amazingly, this strange procedure eventually pulls *any* four-digit number with at least two differing digits to 6174. This number is known as *Kaprekar's constant*. It is the only four-digit number invariant to the rules: $7641 - 1467 = 6174$.

Kaprekar's routine, and the fact that it converges to 6174, can be proven by testing all four-digit numbers with a computer. The Collatz conjecture, on the other hand, certainly *seems* to be true, but despite years of inquiry from many brilliant minds, no one has been able to prove that it is true for all positive integers. After all, a huge integer may exist that never reaches 1; the sequence could simply bounce around forever or eventually hit a repeating cycle that does not include 1.

One way to settle the Collatz conjecture would be to find a counter-example. Obviously, no one has been able to do this. Every number tested has eventually reached 1. Although the destination is always the same, the route can vary. For instance, starting with 5, it only took five steps to reach 1; with 13 it took 9 steps. The number 27 happens to take 111 steps.

The steps are significant because many intriguing patterns arise from the Collatz conjecture. First of all, we can visualize the path that a given integer takes on its journey to 1. Notice that the second rule grows the number while the first rule shrinks it, so the ride can be bumpy. Since the sequence for 5 has already been computed, let's use it as a first example. We'll create a plot where the horizontal axis shows the step progression (a "step" simply refers to a single application of the rules), while the vertical axis displays the number at that step. The points can then be connected to plot out a path.

Recall that the sequence for 5 was: 5, 16, 8, 4, 2, 1. The corresponding plot would look like this:

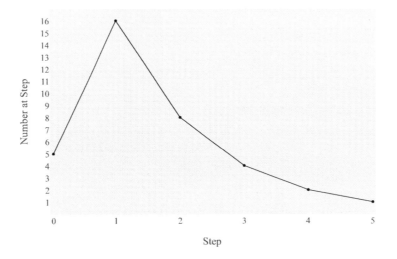

Path to 1 Starting at 5

Compare this to the number 27, which takes much longer to reach 1. Its path can be seen in the next plot:

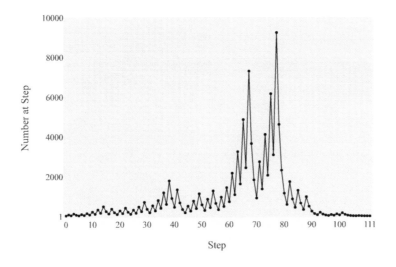

Path to 1 Starting at 27

Notice the large numbers that are reached before eventually falling to 1 at step 111. These paths are sometimes referred to as *hailstone* sequences due to the rise and fall of the numbers, similar to the rise and fall of water droplets in a cloud during hail formation.

The path followed by 27 provides an example of a much longer, more complicated journey toward 1. Larger numbers may take hundreds or thousands of steps before reaching 1. It is not immediately clear from the beginning how many steps will be required, nor how big the numbers will become during the journey.

The number of steps required to reach 1 is itself an intriguing quantity. This is referred to as the *stopping time*. Earlier, we saw that the stopping time of 5 was 5, the stopping time of 13 was 9, and the stopping time of 27 was 111. Mathematicians have long studied the mystifying patterns found in stopping times, and we will explore these patterns as well.

To gather data, we'll compute the stopping times for the integers 1 through 20000. A plot can then be created with the numbers along the horizontal axis and their stopping times on the vertical axis.

The stopping time for 1 is 0 since it is already at 1. For 2, the sequence is just $2, 1$—so the stopping time is 1. For 3, the sequence $3, 10, 5, 16, 8, 4, 2, 1$ is generated—so the stopping time is 7.

The beginning of the stopping time plot will look like this:

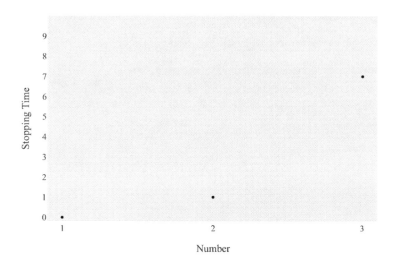

Stopping Time Plot For Integers 1 to 3

We'll continue filling in the stopping times for all integers up to 20000. In order to view all the data within the same plot, we will zoom out and make the point size smaller.

Although the stopping time grows for large numbers, the variation is large. Some numbers less than 2000 exhibit stopping times above 100, while various numbers close to 20000 have stopping times less than 50. The full plot is shown next.

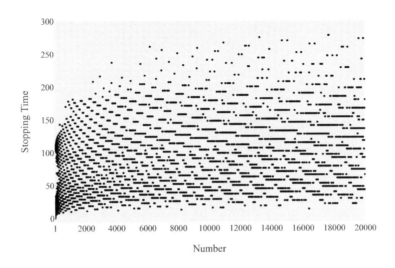

Stopping Time Plot For Integers 1 to 20000

The peculiar horizontal lines of points appearing very close to each other are a standout feature of the plot. They signal the existence of certain "clusters" of numbers that share the same stopping time. For example, the numbers:

$$427, 438, 439, 443, 450$$

all have a stopping time of 53. What is rather surprising is that many larger numbers share this stopping time as well. Some concrete examples are the numbers 19067, 19073, 19081, 19086, and 19087. Furthermore, many clusters of numbers in the 2000s, 15000s, and 16000s share this same stopping time. Popular stopping times manifest as horizontal clusters of points dispersed across the plot.

The stopping time of 53 is only one example; a few other popular stopping times seem to be 48, 58, 128, and 141. Although not obvious from the outset, it appears that the stopping times may have an unforeseen structure.

Finally, let's look at one last quantity of interest—the *highest* integer reached for a given starting number. Looking back at the sequences already calculated, the highest number reached when starting from 5 was 16, and when starting from 13 was 40.

The highest integer reached can be visualized with a plot similar to the one above. Instead of marking the stopping time on the vertical axis, we will instead place a point at the highest number reached. It can be seen on the next page.

A remarkable pattern emerges! Two of the more notable features are the horizontal lines of points, and the diagonal lines rising at different slopes. The horizontal lines signify numbers that appear frequently as the highest number in a sequence. This is rather unexpected since it implies that the paths of certain numbers "meet" and follow identical routes down to 1. For example, there is a horizontal line of points appearing just below 40000 on the vertical axis at the number 39364. It turns out that several starting numbers share this as the highest number in their sequence—the sequences for 447, 511, and 671 all hit 39364 before following the same path down to 1.

26

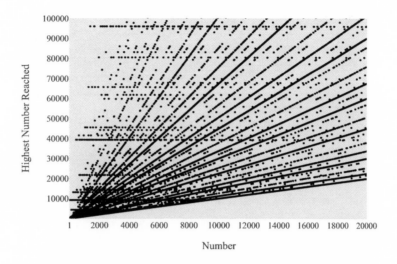

Highest Number Reached For Integers 1 to 20000

As another example, consider the beginning of the dark horizontal line just below 10000 at 9232. Apparently, this is the highest number reached by many smaller starting numbers. Remember the hailstone plot for 27? The highest number attained in that plot was in fact 9232.

The sloping lines aren't as easily explained, but for certain groups of integers, they suggest a steady linear growth rate for the highest number encountered. In any case, the highest number reached certainly reveals another hidden pattern connected to the conjecture.

What is the point of looking at these plots? The lesson here is that mathematics is full of tantalizing patterns, and in many instances, they lead to a deeper understanding of the problem at hand. In this particular case, mathematicians study the patterns above with the hope of uncovering clues to aid in a proof of the Collatz conjecture. Based on experimental evidence, and other more technical arguments, most mathematicians believe that the conjecture is true. And yet, worldwide fame awaits the person who can put the debate to rest once and for all.

Pure mathematical problems, like the Collatz conjecture, are completely detached from the physical world. In this way, they represent something eternal. The strange thing about mathematics is that it also seems to underly the operation of nearly everything in our universe. Therefore, mathematics has the curious distinction of being one of the most abstract branches of human knowledge, but also one of the most useful.

Conway's Game of Life

Letter 2

The purpose of computing is insight, not numbers.
-Richard Hamming

In the 1970s the British mathematician John Conway devised a simple set of rules that led to highly complex and fascinating outcomes. It was dubbed *Conway's Game of Life* due to its uncanny ability to generate lifelike systems. The game even exhibits aspects of mathematical *chaos*, which we'll explore further in a future letter. It has profoundly changed the way scientists view the emergent group behavior of living systems like colonies of ants or flocks of birds. The intriguing aspect of Conway's Game of Life is that it doesn't require any advanced mathematics. In fact, it requires hardly any math at all beyond counting.

In actuality, it is not a game in the traditional sense, but a simple set of rules that are applied over and over. Each application of the rules moves the system forward one generation.

To start, imagine a large grid of squares, like a blank chessboard that goes on forever. We'll refer to each square as a *cell*. Some of the cells will start off "alive" while the others will remain "dead". In the grid below we've arbitrarily chosen the following arrangement of 3 cells to be alive:

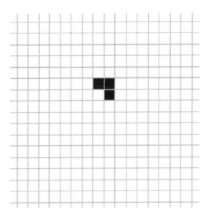

Example Starting with 3 Live Cells: Generation 1

Once the live cells are chosen, the "game" begins. To progress the game the entire grid is scanned, and one of the following four rules is applied to each cell:

1. A live cell with 1 or 0 live neighbors dies as if from loneliness.
2. A live cell with 2 or 3 neighbors lives into the next generation.
3. A live cell with 4 or more neighbors dies as if from overpopulation.
4. Any dead cell with exactly 3 live neighbors comes to life as if from reproduction.

To demonstrate, imagine scanning across the grid one cell at a time. For each cell, the 8 bordering cells that surround it are considered. These 8 cells are its neighbors. The picture below will help illustrate.

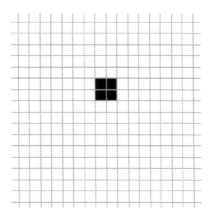

Neighbor Example

The cell marked with an "o" is the cell under consideration, and all the cells marked with an "x" are its neighbors. To decide which rule to apply we simply count how many live neighbors it has. If the rule dictates that the cell stays (or becomes) alive, then the cell is shaded on a new blank grid. If the rule dictates that the cell dies (or remains dead), then the cell is not shaded on the new blank grid. After every cell has been considered, the new grid will be populated with the next generation.

Here is the second generation of the starting grid of 3 cells after the rules have been applied:

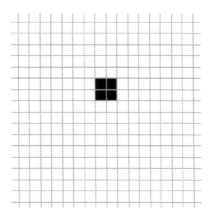

Example Starting with 3 Live Cells: Generation 2

Not only do the 3 original cells live on, but a new one is born.

With some patience, you can convince yourself that this is correct. Look back a page to the original grid of 3 live cells, start scanning from left to right beginning in the upper left corner; just as you would read sentences on a page. As the scanning progresses, all the dead cells remain dead (they would need exactly 3 live neighbors to become alive). Then we hit the first live cell. Notice that it has 2 live neighbors, and according to rule 2 it lives into the next generation. The next live cell directly to the right has 2 live neighbors as well, and also lives on. As scanning continues across the next row we finally hit a dead cell that has 3 live neighbors. According to rule 4, it comes to life (completing the larger black square in the second generation). The final live cell directly to the right remains alive since it has 2 live neighbors.

Now that the second generation has been produced, the new grid can be scanned and the rules applied once again. This will produce the third generation. In this particular case, the third generation isn't very exciting—it's exactly the same as the second generation. Each cell has exactly 3 live neighbors, and so no cell dies, no cell comes to life, and the live cells live on. This two by two square of live cells remain exactly the same forever.

Let's consider another simple example. This time we'll choose 2 cells in a row to be alive:

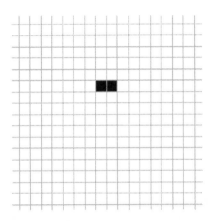

Example Starting with 2 Live Cells: Generation 1

If the rules are applied to create the next generation we end up with:

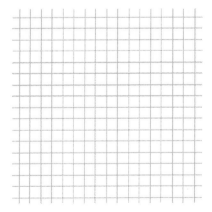

Example Starting with 2 Live Cells: Generation 2

What happened? The two cells died because each of them only had 1 live neighbor. Applying the rules to create further generations is obviously fruitless.

So far nothing very exciting has happened. In the first example, a static group of cells was created after one generation. In the second example, all the cells died after one generation.

Here is a more interesting example. We'll start with the initial configuration of live cells shown below:

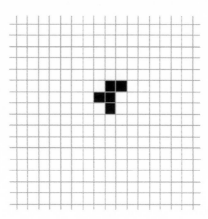

Example Starting with 5 Live Cells: Generation 1

Scanning through the grid and applying the rules creates the second generation. Scanning through the second generation and applying the rules again creates the third generation and so on. Here are the next several generations:

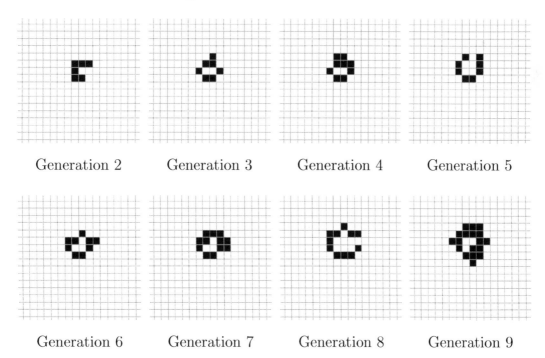

Generation 2   Generation 3   Generation 4   Generation 5

Generation 6   Generation 7   Generation 8   Generation 9

This is certainly more interesting than the first two examples. Various cells spring to life while others blink out of existence as the game advances. It is even more impressive to watch on a computer as a sequence of slides.

As the rules are applied to produce further generations, the cells start to spread around the grid. To see a representation of the grid in the distant future we need to zoom out (remember the grid of squares essentially goes on forever). We'll fast forward to generation 140, only taking snapshots every 10 generations to show the progression more clearly. We'll also omit the grid lines for cleaner images. Quickly moving your eyes from left to right reveals how the cell movements resemble a colony of living organisms, perhaps ants or bacteria. One particular cluster of cells is circled in the first image, we'll explain why in a moment.

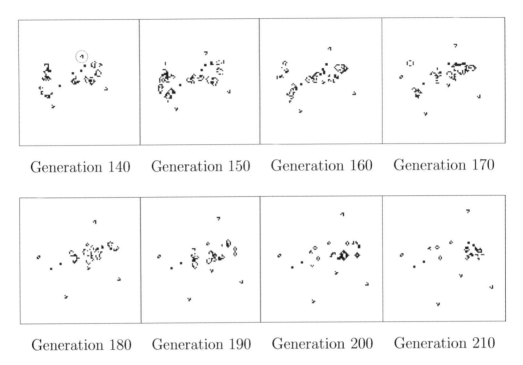

Generation 140   Generation 150   Generation 160   Generation 170

Generation 180   Generation 190   Generation 200   Generation 210

Note the small 5-cell clusters that seem to be moving outward from the larger mass—one of them is circled in the first image as it moves toward the upper-right edge. If the progression is imagined as a short movie, these small clusters would appear to be crawling out across the grid. Only one of them is circled, but there are at least three more in the bottom right area of the last image. They continue moving out into the grid forever, self-sustaining and never-ending. The larger mass of cells continues to evolve for over a thousand generations before a relatively stable state is reached. As it evolves, colonies of cells emerge and various "life forms", like the aforementioned crawling clusters, move off from the main mass.

It is not obvious that such complex ecosystems of cells would evolve from the set of 4 basic rules. Even more amazing is the fact that the images above started from a simple 5 cell configuration. Just imagine the fascinating worlds that can develop from more complex initial arrangements!

This gives a first glimpse into the mathematical concept of *chaos*. A system is deemed chaotic if small changes in starting conditions lead to vastly different outcomes. For instance, suppose a small change is made to the previous initial starting grid of 5 live cells—we'll delete one live cell to get an upside-down 'L' shape.

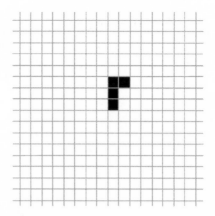

Example Starting with 4 Live Cells: Generation 1

Now let's watch it evolve. Here are the first few generations:

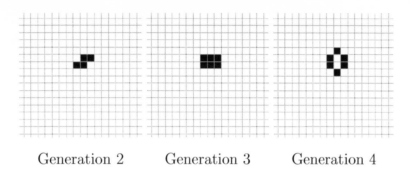

Generation 2   Generation 3   Generation 4

What does generation 5 look like? Since each live cell has exactly 2 live neighbors, it looks exactly the same as generation 4. No new cells are born, no cells die, and the six live cells remain. This contrasts sharply with the previous starting arrangement of 5 cells that grew into a sprawling colony. The initial starting configuration was only changed by 1 cell, and yet the outcome is drastically different. This demonstrates the essential idea behind chaotic systems.

Let's explore a few more initial live cell configurations and see how they evolve.

Here's an initial configuration with 6 live cells:

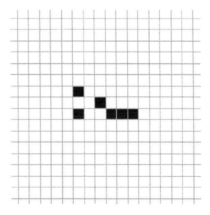

Example Starting with 6 Live Cells: Generation 1

The images below show the progression from one generation to the next:

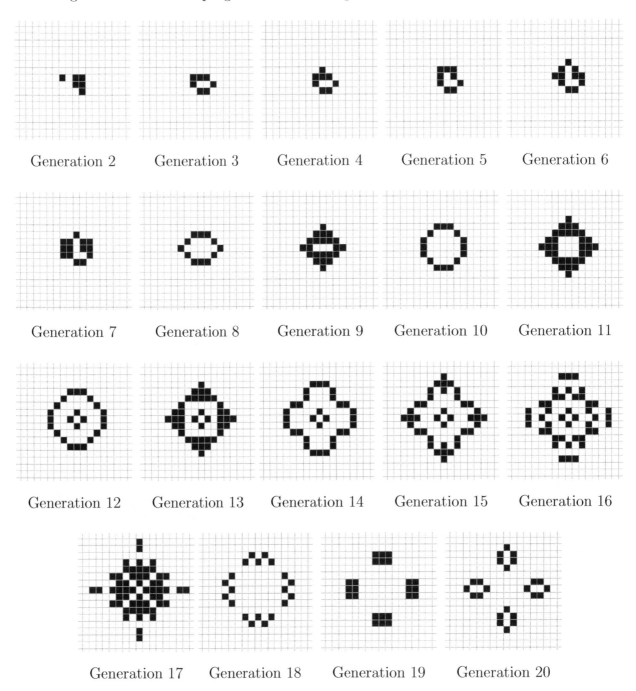

Generation 2   Generation 3   Generation 4   Generation 5   Generation 6

Generation 7   Generation 8   Generation 9   Generation 10   Generation 11

Generation 12   Generation 13   Generation 14   Generation 15   Generation 16

Generation 17   Generation 18   Generation 19   Generation 20

The cells unexpectedly self-organize into a sequence of lovely symmetric patterns! Generation 21 is the same as 20—the cells remain static after this point. A careful scan of generation 20 will show that each live cell has 2 live neighbors.

To demonstrate the sensitivity of initial conditions once again, let's change the starting configuration just slightly. We'll add a single live cell next to the bottom leftmost live cell. Compare this with the previous starting grid of 6 live cells to see that the change is minor.

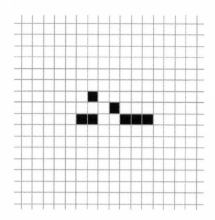

Example Starting with 7 Live Cells: Generation 1

As usual, the rules will be applied to move from one generation to the next:

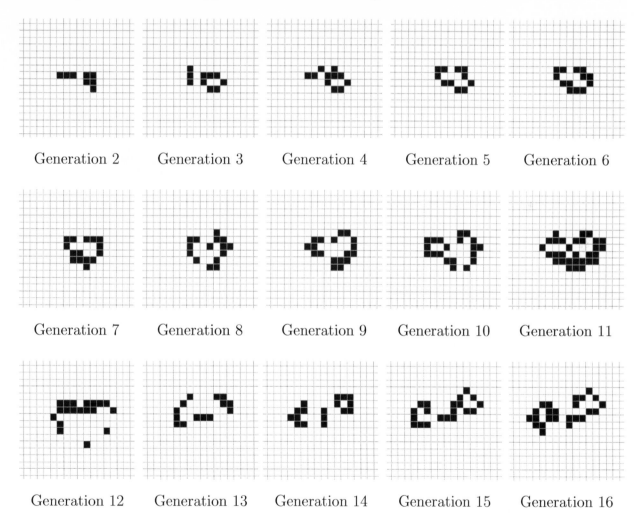

| Generation 2 | Generation 3 | Generation 4 | Generation 5 | Generation 6 |

| Generation 7 | Generation 8 | Generation 9 | Generation 10 | Generation 11 |

| Generation 12 | Generation 13 | Generation 14 | Generation 15 | Generation 16 |

The minor modification breaks the symmetry. Whereas the previous arrangement hit a static state after generation 20, this system keeps evolving for over *five thousand* generations, and shoots off several small clusters that continue moving outward across the grid forever.

There is one brief aside worth mentioning here. A *chaotic* system is much different from a *random* system. In our everyday language these concepts are sometimes used interchangeably. However, a random system is unpredictable, we can't say for certain what the outcome will be. In contrast, a chaotic system is *deterministic*. Given an initial starting condition, one can (at least in theory) compute exactly what it will look like in the future. The strange thing about chaotic systems is that the future looks radically different depending on the initial starting conditions—even if they only differ by the tiniest amount.

Weather patterns provide a common real-world example. Predicting tornados and hurricanes is so difficult because their formation requires just the right conditions. Slight deviations in the environment one day can lead to vastly different results the next. The origin of the maxim "the flap of a butterfly's wings in the Amazon can cause a tornado in Texas" aptly captures this idea, and was coined by the famous scientist Edward Lorenz in the late 1950s as he studied weather prediction. Although scientists can theoretically predict the exact end state of a chaotic system, it is nearly impossible from a practical standpoint.

The artificial "life forms" spawned by Conway's Game of Life have captivated mathematicians, computer scientists, and philosophers for decades. There are infinitely many initial configurations one can devise; some may lead to spectacular life-like activity, while others simply decay into static or oscillating patterns. The visually stunning insight is that highly complex systems can arise from simple rules, yet contain a certain fragility. These insights are striking when considered within the context of the real world. Imagine swarms of bugs, flocks of birds, schools of fish, or even human social dynamics. There is always a possibility that the complex behavior of the group is governed by a set of simple rules followed by each individual.

Sum of the First n Integers

Letter 3

Many who have had an opportunity of knowing any more about mathematics confuse it with arithmetic, and consider it an arid science. In reality, however, it is a science which requires a great amount of imagination.
-Sophie Kowalevski

Quick, try to solve the following sums in your head:

$$1 + 2 + 3 = ?$$
$$1 + 2 + 3 + 4 + 5 = ?$$
$$1 + 2 + 3 + 4 + 5 + 6 + 7 = ?$$

How long did it take to compute these?

What about this one?

$$1 + 2 + 3 + 4 + 5 + 6 + 7 + 8 + 9 + 10 + 11 + 12 + 13 + 14 + 15 + 16 + 17 + 18 + 19 + 20 = ?$$

This last sum is certainly more time-consuming. Even with a calculator, it would take several seconds to punch in all the numbers. The answer is 210.

What if you were asked to sum up the integers 1 through 100? As the numbers grow, the time it takes to compute the sum increases. Summing the numbers 1 through 1000 would take at least 10 times as long. Remarkably, there is a famous formula that collapses this problem into a single computation. It allows these sums to be computed quickly, regardless of how many terms there are.

Our goal is to find the sum of the first n integers.

The symbol n is being used as a placeholder for any positive integer. For instance, choosing $n = 5$ gives the sum of the first 5 integers $1 + 2 + 3 + 4 + 5$, and choosing $n = 20$ gives the sum of the first 20 integers (which we wrote out above).

To begin, let's find the sum with $n = 5$ using a methodology that may seem strange at first sight. We'll write the problem out *twice* and add both copies together, like so:

$$(1 + 2 + 3 + 4 + 5) + (1 + 2 + 3 + 4 + 5)$$

Summing these numbers will of course yield twice the answer we seek.

Note that the terms can be freely rearranged without changing the final answer. That is, the order of the numbers is inconsequential—the sum $1 + 2$ is the same as $2 + 1$. The trick is to rearrange the sum above in a special way. Starting with the outermost two integers, we'll work our way inward forming pairs along the way.

The strategy is illustrated below:

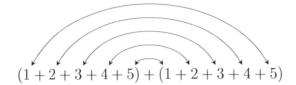

$$(1 + 2 + 3 + 4 + 5) + (1 + 2 + 3 + 4 + 5)$$

Pairing the numbers in this way yields the following rearranged sum:

$$(1 + 5) + (2 + 4) + (3 + 3) + (4 + 2) + (5 + 1)$$

The final sum is precisely the same as before; it still yields twice the answer to $1 + 2 + 3 + 4 + 5$.

Is there anything significant about the terms in parentheses? Each pair of integers sums to exactly 6. How many copies of 6 are there? There is one for each pair, and there is a pair for each of the integers 1 through 5—so there are 5 copies of 6. Summing each pair above gives:

$$6 + 6 + 6 + 6 + 6$$

An alternative way to view these pairs is to write the problem out twice as we did before, but arrange the terms as two sequences of numbers one above the other. One sequence will increment from 1 to 5, and the other will decrement from 5 to 1. Now the pairs can be visualized like this:

$$
\begin{array}{ccccc}
1 & 2 & 3 & 4 & 5 \\
5 & 4 & 3 & 2 & 1 \\
\hline
6 & 6 & 6 & 6 & 6
\end{array}
$$

When viewed from this angle it makes sense that all pairs add to the same number; each time the top row increases by 1, the bottom row decreases by 1. This offset is why the sum of each pair remains constant.

As a second step toward our goal, recall that multiplication is a convenient way to sum several copies of the same number together. Summing 4 copies of the number 3 can be represented as $3 + 3 + 3 + 3 = 4 \cdot 3$. Another example is $5 + 5 = 2 \cdot 5$. The multiplier, then, is the number of times that the integer is repeated in the sum.

Applying this concept to the sum of 6s above gives:

$$6 + 6 + 6 + 6 + 6 = 5 \cdot 6 = 30$$

At this point, with $n = 5$, the answer to *twice* the problem is $5 \cdot 6 = 30$. To correct for this we need to *divide* by 2, producing a final answer of:

$$\frac{5 \cdot 6}{2} = \frac{30}{2} = 15$$

The solution can be confirmed by manually summing $1 + 2 + 3 + 4 + 5 = 15$.

This may seem like a lot of unnecessary work to arrive at an answer; however, we've discovered a very useful pattern that can potentially be used for *any* value of n. Let's try another choice of n to verify.

Using the same trick as before, if $n = 6$ the pairs now add to 7.

$$
\begin{array}{cccccc}
1 & 2 & 3 & 4 & 5 & 6 \\
6 & 5 & 4 & 3 & 2 & 1 \\
\hline
7 & 7 & 7 & 7 & 7 & 7
\end{array}
$$

There are 6 copies of the number 7, and summing them gives:

$$7 + 7 + 7 + 7 + 7 + 7 = 6 \cdot 7 = 42$$

This is twice the answer to the original problem, so we need to divide by 2.

$$\frac{6 \cdot 7}{2} = \frac{42}{2} = 21$$

Once again, the solution can be confirmed by manually summing $1+2+3+4+5+6 = 21$.

Now for the leap of faith—will this pattern work for *any* n? With this question, we arrive at a core tenet of mathematics, which is the discovery of a pattern that holds true for any input. To convince ourselves that the pattern does indeed hold true for any n, let's imagine writing out two rows of numbers just as we've done for $n = 5$ and $n = 6$. The first row will count up from 1 to n and the second row will count down from n to 1. In every case each column will add up to $n + 1$. With $n = 5$ the columns added to (substituting 5 in place of n) $5 + 1 = 6$, and with $n = 6$ the columns added to $6 + 1 = 7$. For any n, each column will *always* add to $n + 1$.

Now imagine summing all resulting copies of the number $n + 1$. There is one copy for each of the n columns. Adding them all together gives $n \cdot (n + 1)$. Remember that with $n = 5$ each column summed to $5 + 1 = 6$. There were 5 columns, and adding all the 6s together gave $5 \cdot 6$. This is precisely what the formula $n \cdot (n + 1)$ gives when n is replaced with 5. Using yet another example from above, when $n = 6$ each column summed to $6 + 1 = 7$. There were 6 columns, so summing all the 7s gave $6 \cdot 7$. Replacing n with 6 in the formula $n \cdot (n + 1)$ gives the same answer. This formula works for any integer n.

The last step, like before, is to correct for the fact that we arrive at twice the answer to the original problem when all the numbers are summed. In other words, the formula $n \cdot (n + 1)$ for the sum of all columns is double the solution we seek; therefore, we must divide $n \cdot (n+1)$ by 2.

The famous solution for the sum of the first n integers can finally be assembled:

$$1 + 2 + 3 + ... + n = \frac{n \cdot (n + 1)}{2}$$

In mathematics, the three dots between the 3 and the n above signify the continuation of a pattern. In this case, they stand in for "continue adding together all the integers up to n".

This formula is so useful because it works for *any* integer n, as can be verified with a few examples. Earlier, we asked for the sum of the first 20 integers. Plugging $n = 20$ into the formula gives:

$$1 + 2 + 3 + \ldots + 20 = \frac{20 \cdot (20 + 1)}{2} = \frac{20 \cdot 21}{2} = \frac{420}{2} = 210$$

We end up with the correct answer of 210.

How about the sum of the integers 1 through 100? This would take several minutes to compute by hand, but the formula yields the answer in a few seconds. Plugging in $n = 100$ gives:

$$1 + 2 + 3 + \ldots + 100 = \frac{100 \cdot (100 + 1)}{2} = \frac{100 \cdot 101}{2} = \frac{10100}{2} = 5050$$

Take a moment to appreciate the power of this formula. A problem that would have otherwise been extraordinarily difficult, like summing the integers 1 to one million, has been reduced to a trivial calculation. Armed with a calculator but no knowledge of this formula, it would take days to compute this sum. However, now that the hidden pattern within the problem has been discovered, we could compute the answer in a matter of seconds.

When exploring mathematical concepts, there are often wide-ranging and unexpected connections between different ideas. We'll briefly explore two ideas related to the sum of the first n integers—triangular numbers and the handshake problem.

Most people are familiar with square numbers such as $2^2 = 4$, $3^2 = 9$, $4^2 = 16$ and so on. Square numbers represent the area of a square with a given side length; 9 is the area of a square with side length 3 and 16 is the area of a square with side length 4.

There is another geometric way to visualize square numbers. Each square number can be represented by a series of dots arranged into a perfect square. For example, here is the number $5^2 = 25$ represented with 25 dots:

Less familiar, are the *triangular numbers*, cousins of the square numbers. The first few triangular numbers are 1, 3, 6, 10, and 15. Just as square numbers can be represented as dots arranged in a square, triangular numbers can be represented as equilateral triangles, which by definition have all equal sides. Here is the equilateral triangle for the triangular number 15:

Carefully count the dots in the triangle above. Starting from the top with 1 dot, then 2 dots, then 3, and so on until the bottom is reached with 5 dots. Summing all the dots leads to the triangular number $15 = 1 + 2 + 3 + 4 + 5$.

To produce a square number the formula is easy: take an integer and square it (multiply it by itself). What about producing triangular numbers? It turns out that the formula for triangular numbers is the same formula we derived for the sum of the first n integers. It isn't too difficult to see why. The example above shows that triangular numbers can be computed by counting the dots starting from the top row and moving to the bottom row. The final sum of dots is $1 + 2 + 3 + ... + n$.

So the formula:
$$\frac{n \cdot (n+1)}{2}$$

produces triangular numbers. Instead of counting dots, plugging in $n = 5$ produces the triangular number 15:
$$\frac{5 \cdot (5+1)}{2} = \frac{5 \cdot 6}{2} = \frac{30}{2} = 15$$

Note that bowling makes use of the 4th triangular number $\frac{4 \cdot (4+1)}{2} = 10$ to ensure that the pins can be arranged in an equilateral triangle.

It turns out that the triangular numbers are closely related to the square numbers. Look what happens if two *consecutive* triangular numbers are summed:

$$1 + 3 = 4$$
$$3 + 6 = 9$$
$$6 + 10 = 16$$
$$10 + 15 = 25$$

We end up with the square numbers! This can be seen geometrically by studying the square of dots representing the square number 25. If it is split diagonally two triangles of dots are obtained, one containing 10 and the other 15. In fact, every square number can be split into two consecutive triangular numbers.

There is one last interesting item we'll mention. The triangular numbers, and therefore the sum of the first n integers, also provide a solution to the *handshake problem*—a famous problem from the mathematical field of combinatorics. The handshake problem asks: In a group of n people, how many handshakes must take place for everyone to shake hands exactly once?

Suppose there are 5 people whom we'll label A, B, C, D, and E. To visualize the handshake possibilities we'll arrange the labels in a square grid.

	A	B	C	D	E
A					
B					
C					
D					
E					

With this arrangement it is easy to pair people for handshakes. Starting in the first row with person A we'll move across the columns. If A has not shaken hands with the person in that column we'll draw a dot •. For the first row, everyone except A (since you do not shake hands with yourself) will get a dot. Then A will be done shaking hands.

	A	B	C	D	E
A		•	•	•	•
B					
C					
D					
E					

Now move to the second row with person B. A already shook hands with B (as marked above), and of course B will not shake her own hand, so B will only need to shake hands with C, D, and E.

	A	B	C	D	E
A		•	•	•	•
B			•	•	•
C					
D					
E					

Next, person C already shook hands with both A and B, so he only needs to shake hands with D and E. If this logic is applied to the remaining rows, we end up with the final table shown below.

	A	B	C	D	E
A		•	•	•	•
B			•	•	•
C				•	•
D					•
E					

Notice that E doesn't have any dots, because by the time we get to the last row, E has already shaken everyone's hand. The solution to the handshake problem with 5 people can now be solved by counting the dots; there are 10 of them.

Is there anything familiar about the number 10 and the shape of the dots above? Although it is rotated due to the positioning of the table, a triangle shape clearly emerges.

The answer to the handshake problem with n people is precisely the $(n-1)$th triangular number. The 1 subtracted from n accounts for the fact that no one shakes their own hand.

For the case of $n = 5$ people sketched above, the answer should be the $(n-1)$th triangular number, which here is $(5-1) = 4$. Plugging in $n = 4$ using our handy formula:

$$\frac{n \cdot (n+1)}{2}$$

gives:

$$\frac{4 \cdot (4+1)}{2} = \frac{4 \cdot 5}{2} = \frac{20}{2} = 10$$

This matches our answer derived from the grid of 5 people.

With a group of 23 people, exactly $\frac{22 \cdot 23}{2} = 253$ handshakes would need to take place for everyone to meet. Incidentally, this is the key piece of information revealing the paradox behind the famous "birthday problem". The birthday problem asks: what is the smallest group size you would need so that the probability of 2 or more people sharing the same birthday is greater than 50%? Intuition suggests that the group size would need to be fairly large, perhaps a couple hundred. The actual answer is surprisingly low, only 23.

This is an instance where our intuition leads us astray. That's because most of us only think about comparing our *own* birthday to all others. However, there are far more comparisons taking place; 253 to be exact, and that is enough to push the probability of at least one person finding a match over 50%.

Who would have guessed that the sum of the first n integers would yield such a useful formula and have connections to triangles and combinatorics? Mathematics is full of hidden patterns like the ones we've just seen, and problems that appear complicated at first glance can often be untangled with a few key insights.

The most important detail of this letter is the use of the symbol n. The overarching goal of mathematics, and nearly every other branch of science, is to observe specific patterns and try to generalize them. In this case, we noticed a pattern when the sum of the first 5 integers was written twice and rearranged. It also happened to work for the sum of the first 6 integers. This leads quite naturally to the question of whether a similar pattern holds for all integers.

There are infinitely many integers, and we can't possibly check them all. Instead, mathematicians started using symbols to stand in for numbers—freeing them from having to choose a specific quantity like 5 or 6. The letter n was chosen here, but the actual letter is not important. Traditionally, mathematicians use letters like n and m when dealing with integers, and letters like x and y when dealing with decimal numbers.

Random Sampling & Buffon's Needle

Letter 4

The moving power of mathematical invention is not reasoning but imagination.
-Augustus de Morgan

Randomness is normally viewed as an undesirable aspect of our daily lives. It's hard to plan ahead when unpredictable events like traffic jams, illness, or flight delays disrupt our plans. Scientists have a similar disdain for randomness. To make accurate inferences, experiments need to be repeatable—with as few variables left to chance as possible. However, there are some situations where randomness can be harnessed to produce both useful and unexpected results.

To begin, we'll focus on a simple practical problem—computing the area of a shape. Let's review a situation where the formula is easy to work out. If a rectangle measures 10 by 7, then multiplying length times width gives a total area of $10 \cdot 7 = 70$. This formula is straightforward and intuitive.

Rectangle with Area $10 \cdot 7 = 70$

If we move away from straight lines, the task of finding the area is a bit more complicated. Consider a circle with radius 1.

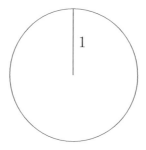

Circle with Radius 1

44

Unlike rectangles, computing the area of a curved shape isn't so obvious, and usually requires the use of a memorized formula. In this case, the formula for the area of a circle is $\pi \cdot r^2$ where r is the radius. So the area of the circle above is simply $\pi \cdot 1^2 = \pi = 3.14159$ (rounded to five decimal places).

Now suppose we didn't know this formula. How could the area of the circle be determined?

One approach is to approximate it with something more manageable, like a square:

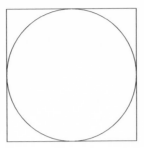

Circle Enclosed by Square

The square has side lengths equal to the diameter of the circle. Recall that the diameter is just twice the radius of 1, so the diameter is 2 and therefore the square has sides of length 2. We already know how to compute the area of a square—it is $2 \cdot 2 = 4$. This isn't a very good approximation, but since the circle resides within the square, it must have an area less than 4.

To obtain a better approximation we can use polygons with more sides, like a hexagon (six sides) or an octagon (eight sides):

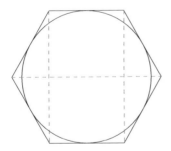 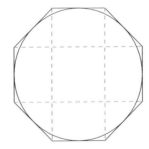

The polygons can be subdivided into shapes made of straight lines, like the rectangles and right triangles delineated by the dashed lines above. We know how to compute the area of these straight-lined shapes, and by computing the area of each one we can work out a better approximation for the area of the circle. As polygons with more sides are used the approximation becomes more precise. Unfortunately, this is tedious work, and the work increases with the number of sides.

There exists an entirely different approach, which despite its unintuitive nature, uses randomness to estimate a fixed quantity.

Let's use the same idea of a circle enclosed in a square. Now imagine randomly tossing a small coin onto the surface of the square. When the coin lands, pick it up and mark where it fell with a small dot. This will be done repeatedly, and in the end we'll count up how many times the coin landed within the circle.

Suppose the coin is tossed onto the square 10 times. For each toss, the landing place is marked with a small dot as shown below:

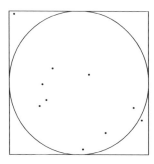

10 Random Points

In this particular example, the coin landed within the circle 8 times. Now take this number, divide by 10 (the total number of tosses), and multiply by 4. Dividing by the number of tosses and multiplying by 4 will be explained later.

$$\left(\frac{8}{10}\right) \cdot 4 = 3.2$$

The resulting number 3.2 isn't too far from the true value of π. What is rather surprising is that this number will move closer to π the more times the coin is tossed.

If the number of tosses is increased to 1000, the result is a decent approximation to π. It's important to remember that this is a *random* process, and tossing the coin another 1000 times would yield a slightly different number. The following images show two trials of 1000 random tosses each.

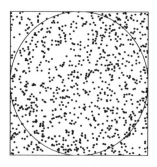 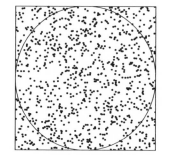

1000 Random Points   1000 Random Points
Trial 1   Trial 2

In the first trial, the coin landed within the circle 787 times. In the second trial, it landed within the circle 791 times. Dividing by the number of tosses and multiplying by 4 as before produces two more approximations of π:

$$4 \cdot \left(\frac{787}{1000}\right) = 3.148$$

$$4 \cdot \left(\frac{791}{1000}\right) = 3.164$$

If the number of tosses is increased to 100000, the difference between the results and the true value of π narrows significantly. Below is the outcome of two such trials of 100000 tosses each. The picture is omitted because there are too many points—it would just look like a solid black square.

In the first trial, the coin landed within the circle 78506 times; in the second, it landed within the circle 78588 times. Dividing by the total number of tosses and multiplying by 4 yields two more approximations to π.

$$4 \cdot \left(\frac{78506}{100000}\right) = 3.14024$$

$$4 \cdot \left(\frac{78588}{100000}\right) = 3.14352$$

We are now approximating π to two decimal places.

Why does this work? This is an example of a more general class of techniques known as *Monte Carlo* methods—a way of using random sampling to estimate fixed numerical quantities. The name is a nod to the Monte Carlo Casino in Monaco, where random processes abound in the form of gambling. Usually, the numerical quantity to be estimated is extremely difficult to compute using standard methods (i.e. no formula exists).

The key concept here is *random sampling*. Choosing a random point within the square and recording if it falls within the circle is akin to sampling a small piece of information about the circle. Specifically, how much space it occupies within the square. By ensuring that the points are random, the entire space of the circle is "explored". Finally, all these bits of information are combined to obtain an estimate for the area of the circle.

This leads to another question: what kind of information is gleaned from each random point? Well, each point has some *probability* of falling within the enclosed circle. What is this probability? It is the proportion of the area within the square that the circle takes up. The square has total area 4, so the probability of a random point landing within the circle is $\frac{\text{circle area}}{\text{square area}} = \frac{\text{circle area}}{4}$. In other words:

$$\text{probability of landing in circle} = \frac{\text{circle area}}{4}$$

Another way to write this is:

$$4 \cdot (\text{probability of landing in circle}) = \text{circle area}$$

The equation above says that if we can estimate the probability of landing in the circle then we can multiply by 4 to estimate its area. This is the origin of the 4 in the previous computations.

Counting the number of times the coin lands within the circle and dividing by the total number of tosses is one easy way to estimate the probability of landing in the circle. This is similar in spirit to estimating more mundane probabilities, like the chance of rolling a particular number, say 1, on a six-sided die. To achieve this, we could roll the die a large number of times and count the number of 1s that appear. If it was rolled 100 times and came to rest on 1 for 18 of those rolls, then the probability of rolling a 1 is likely around $\frac{18}{100} = .18$ (the precise probability is .1666, but .18 isn't too far off). Rolling it 1000 times would achieve an even better estimate.

The Monte Carlo method relies on constructing an artificial game of chance where the probability of some result (a point falling within the circle) relates directly to a quantity we're trying to estimate (the area of the circle). This is a powerful idea, and although we already knew the area of the circle, this same setup can be used to estimate the areas of weird shapes that defy conventional methods of computation.

Consider the ellipse shape shown below.

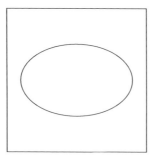

Ellipse Enclosed by Square

What is the area of this ellipse? The formula for the area of a circle is fairly well known, but not many people will readily recall the formula for the area of an ellipse. Regardless, our method doesn't care what kind of shape is drawn. We can always estimate its area using random sampling.

The square is the same size—it has total area $2 \cdot 2 = 4$. The area of the ellipse is unknown, but we do know that the probability of a random point falling within the ellipse is $\frac{\text{area of ellipse}}{\text{area of square}} = \frac{\text{area of ellipse}}{4}$. Here are 1000 randomly selected points:

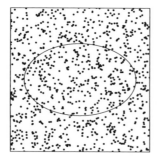

1000 Random Points

In this case, 316 points fall within the ellipse. Dividing by the total number of points and multiplying by 4 as we did earlier gives the approximate area of the ellipse:

$$4 \cdot \frac{316}{1000} = 1.264$$

The result is quite close to the true area, which happens to be 1.2566 rounded to four decimal places.

So far, the examples have focused on rather simple geometric shapes. However, the power of random sampling has been known for centuries, and fascinating schemes have been devised over the years. One setup of particular renown is known as *Buffon's Needle Problem*; it is an intriguing example of the unexpected connections that often arise in mathematics.

Imagine a wooden floor where the planks are all the same width, and a small sewing needle that is as long as the planks are wide. Now randomly toss the needle onto the floor. Regardless of where it lands, it will either lie entirely on a single plank, or it will lie across two planks. The two possible scenarios are illustrated below:

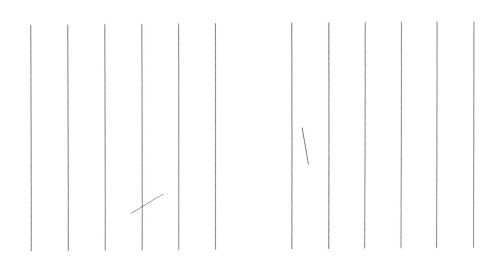

Needle Crosses Planks   Needle Does Not Cross Planks

Of course, the precise position of the needle will be random, but these are the only two possibilities. Either it crosses two planks, or it does not.

Similar to the circle example we'll randomly toss the needle a large number of times, and after each toss, we'll record if it came to rest crossing two planks. Finally, we'll compute the number:

$$2 \cdot \left(\frac{\text{\# Tosses}}{\text{\# Times Crosses Planks}} \right)$$

The multiplier of 2 isn't overly important—it plays a role similar to the multiplier of 4 in the previous examples. The numerator "# Tosses" is the total number of tosses, and the denominator "# Times Crosses Planks" is the number of times the needle landed across two planks.

Now watch what happens when this scenario is simulated. We'll perform 5 experiments where the needle is randomly tossed onto the floor 100, 1000, 10000, 100000, and finally 1000000 times. The results appear in the table below:

# Tosses	# Times Crosses Planks	$2 \cdot \left(\dfrac{\text{\# Tosses}}{\text{\# Times Crosses Planks}} \right)$
100	62	3.2258
1000	627	3.1898
10000	6388	3.1309
100000	63659	3.1417
1000000	636656	3.1414

Amazingly, the number in the right column seems to converge to π (and it can be proven that it does), but there are no circles to be found, only straight lines! The connection between randomly tossing a needle onto a wooden plank floor and the area of a circle is completely unexpected, and it's what makes Buffon's Needle Problem so astounding.

That being said, whenever π is encountered, you can bet that there is a circle hiding somewhere. It is far from obvious where the circle is found, but we can provide a hint.

What happens if the needle is randomly tossed many times while ensuring that the center point is fixed? If the position of the needle was traced for several tosses we'd end up with something like this:

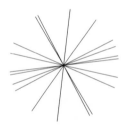

10 Random Needle Tosses with Fixed Center

In essence, this is where the circle is hiding in Buffon's Needle Problem. This is far from a complete explanation, but it sheds a bit of light on the mystery.

Buffon's Needle Problem is an example of a truly unexpected result in mathematics. The surprise is two-fold. First, the fact that this random process converges to anything at all is remarkable in its own right. Second, even though the needle and floorboards are made entirely of straight lines, it converges to the area of a *circle*.

The use of randomness is a common technique in many areas of applied mathematics. The basic idea is brilliant: set up an artificial game of chance where the probability of an outcome is directly related to the unknown quantity you wish to estimate. The probability can then be approximated using random sampling. Although unconventional at first glance, this idea allows scientists to estimate quantities that are otherwise impossible to compute using classical formulas.

The main takeaway is not a deep understanding of the formulas, but rather the insight that many small pieces of information can be combined into something useful. The entire field of *statistics* is dedicated to this idea, and it will be revisited in a future letter.

Feedback Loops & Chaos
Letter 5

Mathematics is the most beautiful and most powerful creation of the human spirit.
–Stefan Banach

When feedback loops arise in the real world they often exhibit rather bizarre behavior. The unintended high-pitched screeching generated by a microphone loudspeaker system is one common example. The amplified sound from the speaker is picked up by the microphone, which in turn emits it through the speaker, only to be picked up by the microphone once again. This infinite audio loop culminates, usually rather quickly, in a distinct high-pitched sound.

For a visual example of a feedback loop, consider what happens when two mirrors are placed opposite from one another. If you manage a peek into one of the mirrors you will see an infinite progression of reflections. The first mirror reflects the image of the second mirror which reflects the image of the first mirror and so on forever. Kaleidoscopes take advantage of a similar property to produce colorful symmetric images.

As these examples illustrate, the outcomes of feedback loops can be peculiar. Under the right conditions, they can even lead to a particular type of behavior known as *chaos* (we touched on chaotic behavior in a past letter on Conway's Game of Life). Recall that a system is deemed chaotic if slight changes in starting conditions lead to vastly different outcomes. Feedback loops are the perfect medium for this type of phenomenon. Small changes tend to be amplified as the feedback loop advances. Conway's Game of Life was itself a kind of feedback loop, each generation conceived from the one preceding it.

The notion of a feedback loop can be represented quite nicely with a mathematical *function*. For our purposes, a function is an expression where one number acts as the input and another number is returned as the output. Here are two example functions:

1. $1 + x$
2. x^2

The x is a placeholder for any number. Plugging 1 into the first function gives $1 + 1 = 2$, and plugging in .5 gives $1 + .5 = 1.5$. The function simply adds 1 to the input. The second function squares a number. Plugging in 2 gives $2^2 = 4$ and plugging in 5 gives $5^2 = 25$. A function takes in a number, applies some operations, and yields a result.

What do functions have to do with feedback loops? Well, since any number can act as the input for a function, there is no reason we can't take the output number and use it as the new input. To start the feedback loop however, we need to choose a number to begin with. Let's choose 1 as the starting point and create a feedback loop with the function $x + 1$. Plugging in 1 yields $1 + 1 = 2$. Taking the output of 2 and using it as the new input gives $2 + 1 = 3$. Now using 3 as the new input gives $3 + 1 = 4$ and so on. The feedback loop generates the numbers (starting with the original input 1):

$$1, 2, 3, 4, \ldots$$

Different functions create different feedback loops, and some will be more exciting than others. In this case, regardless of the starting value, the function $1 + x$ doesn't create very interesting sequences; the numbers simply grow by 1.

The function x^2 is a bit more compelling. If we choose a starting number larger than 1 then the sequence grows forever. For example, starting with 2 gives $2^2 = 4$. With 4 as the new input the next term is $4^2 = 16$, and using 16 gives $16^2 = 256$. This feedback loop grows quite rapidly:

$$2, 4, 16, 256, \ldots$$

Starting with a number between 0 and 1 on the other hand, produces a shrinking feedback loop. Plugging in .5 as the initial value gives $.5^2 = .25$. Using .25 as the new input yields $.25^2 = .0625$, and using .0625 gives $.0625^2 = 0.00390625$. The first few elements of the feedback loop are:

$$.5, .25, .0625, 0.00390625, \ldots$$

This is the first feedback loop where the numbers seem to be shrinking. In fact, a feedback loop for the function x^2 initialized with any number between 0 and 1 will eventually *converge* to 0. In other words, if the feedback loop continues indefinitely, the numbers will eventually be so small that they'll be indistinguishable from 0.

The number 0 is like a black hole for feedback loops created with x^2; any feedback loop using this function, and initiated with a starting value between 0 and 1, will eventually be pulled to 0. This is akin to the microphone screeching problem. If the right sound (i.e. the starting value) from the speaker is picked up by the microphone, then the feedback loop converges to a single high-pitched noise.

We will now define a simple yet remarkable function:

$$c \cdot x \cdot (1 - x)$$

Part of this should look familiar because $x \cdot (1 - x)$ is just a function like any other. It takes a number and multiplies it by one minus that number. The letter c is the only new part. The idea is to replace c with a fixed number and make use of the resulting function. For example, we could fix c at 2 and use the function $2 \cdot x \cdot (1 - x)$, or we could fix c at 2.7 and use the function $2.7 \cdot x \cdot (1 - x)$. With each choice of c we obtain a function to use for feedback loops.

Our goal is to explore the eventual behavior of these related functions. It turns out that the feedback loops are particularly interesting when c is fixed to a number in the range 2.5 to 4.

The starting value for x will not be particularly important—we could easily choose from many numbers, but we'll keep it simple and always start with .5. For easier reading, we'll also round all numbers to 5 decimal places when printed.

Let's start with c fixed at 2.5. This yields the function:

$$2.5 \cdot x \cdot (1 - x)$$

We'll create a feedback loop initialized with .5 by plugging in $x = .5$ to get:

$$2.5 \cdot .5 \cdot (1 - .5) = .625$$

Now .625 will act as the new input to produce:

$$2.5 \cdot .625 \cdot (1 - .625) = .58594$$

In each step along the way the function's output is used as the new input. Continuing on like this, the first several terms of the feedback loop are:

$$.5, .625, .58594, .60654, .59662, .60166, .59916, .60042, .59979,$$
$$.6001, .59995, .60003, .59999, .60001, .6, .6, .6$$

As it advances, the values are drawn to the number .6. Once a value is reached where the input is returned as the output, the sequence will continue like this forever. Although we're initializing with the value .5, it turns out that many other starting values near .5 are pulled to the same value of .6.

Let's choose another value of c and repeat this experiment. We'll try $c = 2.6$, which yields the function:

$$2.6 \cdot x \cdot (1 - x)$$

Initiating the feedback loop with $x = .5$, the first several terms are:

$$.5, .65, .5915, .62823, .60725, .6201, .6125, .61709, .61435, .616, .61501.61561, .61525,$$
$$.61546, .61534, .61541, .61537, .61539, .61538, .61538, .61538$$

It takes slightly longer to get there, but the sequence settles down near the value .61538.

You might be wondering if all feedback loops initiated with .5 eventually settle down to a single fixed number—regardless of the choice of c. It turns out that this is not the case; for instance, consider setting $c = 3.2$ to get the function:

$$3.2 \cdot x \cdot (1 - x)$$

Here are the first several terms of the feedback loop, starting with the initial value of .5:

$$.5, .8, .512, .79954, .51288.79947, .51302, .79946, .51304, .79946, .51304, .79946$$

We haven't seen this type of behavior before! It quickly converges to an oscillating sequence of two numbers, .51304 and .79946.

Another oscillating sequence occurs with the choice $c = 3.3$:

$$3.3 \cdot x \cdot (1 - x)$$

The first several terms are:

.5, .825, .47644, .82317, .48036, .82373, .47916, .82357, .4795
.82361, .4794, .8236, .47943, .8236, .47943, .8236, .47943

The two eventual repeating numbers are now .8236 and .47943. Just as with a single point, once an oscillating sequence of points is hit, the sequence will continue like that forever.

Our main interest lies in the long-term behavior of these sequences. So far, two types of behavior have emerged. With values of c equal to 2.5 and 2.6, the sequence eventually settles down to a single number; for values of c equal to 3.2 and 3.3, the sequence eventually oscillates between two numbers. Ultimately, we'd like to *visualize* the long-term behavior of these feedback loops as c varies.

This can be accomplished with a simple plotting technique. Along the horizontal axis will appear values of c, and for each of those values we'll compute a feedback loop initialized with .5. On the vertical axis, we'll plot the eventual behavior of the loop.

This is easier to comprehend if we start with a simple version of the plot using the four values of c already chosen:

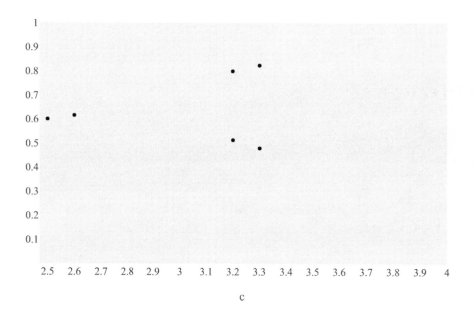

Eventual Feedback Loop Behavior for Example Values of c

Recall that the feedback loop for $c = 2.5$ converged to .6. At $c = 2.5$ on the horizontal axis there is a single point at .6. Similarly for $c = 2.6$, there is a single point at .61538. Notice that there are two points above both $c = 3.2$ and $c = 3.3$. These represent the oscillating points for those choices of c. The points above 3.2 are located at .51304 and .79946, and the points above 3.3 are at .47943 and .8236. Let's fill in the remaining values of c between 2.5 and 3.3. We'll make the point sizes smaller to fit them nicely on the plot.

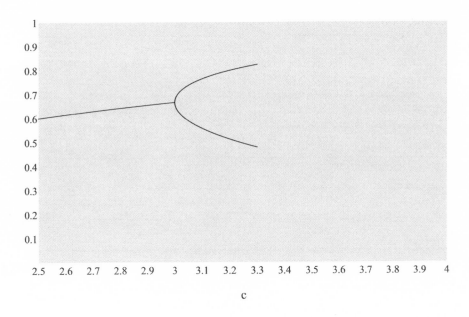

Eventual Feedback Loop Behavior for Values of c Between 2.5 and 3.3

The shape that emerges is not totally unexpected. It appears that for values of c less than about 3, the feedback loops eventually converge to a single number. Starting with .6 for $c = 2.5$ the values rise slowly to around .65 as c approaches 3. For values of c in the approximate range of 3 to 3.3 the feedback loop oscillates between two points. Again, the two points change slightly as c grows. By the time c is near 3.3, the oscillating points are around .5 and .8.

What does the plot look like for values of c beyond 3.3? The result is quite surprising—the completed plot appears next:

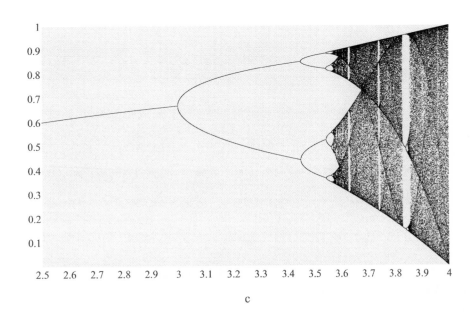

Eventual Feedback Loop Behavior for Values of c

This is an extraordinary picture! Just before $c = 3.5$ the feedback loop starts oscillating between four values instead of two. If you look closely near $c = 3.6$, the behavior changes once again; now oscillation occurs between eight different points. After approximately $c = 3.6$, everything changes.

While feedback loops with c less than about 3.6 eventually converge to a handful of points, beyond this value is the onset of utter chaos. These feedback loops fail to display any discernible pattern, oscillating wildly through a seemingly random sequence of numbers without ever settling down. In fact, this is one of the most visually striking examples of mathematical chaos; small changes in the parameter c lead to vastly different outcomes.

One of the most intriguing aspects of many chaotic processes is that there seems to be *some* kind of underlying structure woven into the chaos. To truly appreciate this, consider the following magnified plot for values of c between 3.6 and 3.7. We've stretched it out horizontally to reveal more detail.

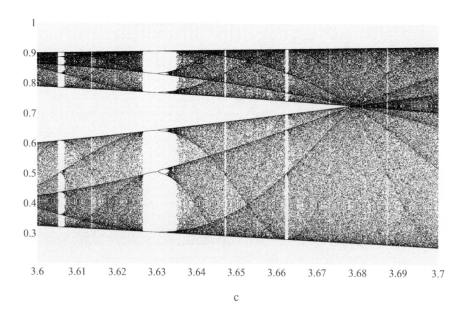

Zoomed View for c Between 3.6 and 3.7

Recall that a very small dot is drawn for each number in the eventual feedback loop. In some feedback loops, a cluster of numbers will show up more often than others; these clusters manifest as darker shades in the plot. The wave-like curves above are created by this phenomenon.

There is another mysterious detail here. Every so often, a gap occurs. These gaps are areas where the feedback loop temporarily settles down into non-chaotic behavior. To explore these areas further, let's zoom into the first noticeable gap on the plot near $c = 3.63$. Look at the numbers on the axes of the next plot, and compare them to the plot on this page. We've enlarged the lower middle portion of the large gap near $c = 3.63$ on the horizontal axis, and near .5 on the vertical axis.

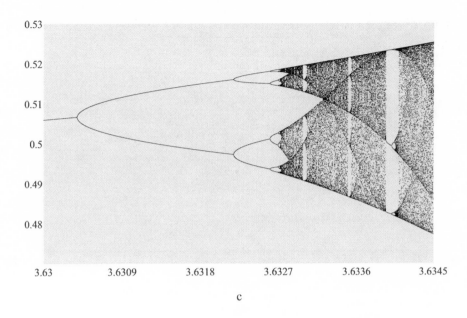

Zoomed View for c Between 3.63 and 3.6345

Does this look familiar? Incredibly, this tiny magnified portion of the plot looks like a mini version of the original. This can be taken even further by zooming into a tiny portion of *this* plot to see another very similar image. This type of self-similarity often arises in *fractals*, and in fact chaos and fractals are closely related. We'll explore fractals more deeply in a future letter.

When mathematicians refer to the "beauty" of mathematics, they could mean many things. In some cases, appreciating the beauty of a mathematical result requires years of study. That is not the case here; these images can be appreciated without knowing where they come from. Paradoxically, knowing that these images are produced from simple functions only deepens the mystery!

Continuous Growth & e

Letter 6

Any fool can know. The point is to understand.
-Albert Einstein

Growth rate estimation is an important step in many mathematical modeling techniques. Predicting the future size of a bacteria colony, or the ending balance of an interest-bearing bank account, both require accurate growth rates. While growth can occur in myriad ways, there is a subtle variety often observed in nature whose analysis leads to one of the most famous numbers in mathematics.

Before turning to the type of growth mentioned above, let's review a scenario that shows how easy it is to arrive at extreme outcomes. Envision a standard chessboard containing 64 squares. Now place 2 grains of rice on the first square, 4 grains on the second, 8 on the third, and so on, doubling the grains on each subsequent square. How many grains of rice will the last square contain? The math is not difficult to understand; each move multiplies the quantity by 2. Surprisingly, by the time the last square is reached, the amount of rice is mind-boggling—it is on the order of hundreds of billions of tons. Even if the entire world crop were stockpiled for a *century* it would not be enough to represent this quantity. Needless to say, this is more than intuition would suggest.

Despite the simple math of the chessboard example, growth rates of this kind cannot possibly occur for long periods of time in the real world. However, we can use this example to illustrate a useful calculation and review what it means to raise a number to a power.

The number of grains for the first several chess squares can be computed as:

$$\text{(Square 1)} \quad 2$$
$$\text{(Square 2)} \quad 2 \cdot 2$$
$$\text{(Square 3)} \quad 2 \cdot 2 \cdot 2$$
$$\text{(Square 4)} \quad 2 \cdot 2 \cdot 2 \cdot 2$$

Raising a number to a power is shorthand for multiplying the number by itself several times, so this can be expressed using powers as:

$$\text{(Square 1)} \quad 2^1$$
$$\text{(Square 2)} \quad 2^2$$
$$\text{(Square 3)} \quad 2^3$$
$$\text{(Square 4)} \quad 2^4$$

The term 2^4 is read as "two raised to the fourth power".

The increasing powers signify moving from one square to the next—each move increases the power by 1, so the number of grains by the 4th square is:

$$16 = 2 \cdot 2 \cdot 2 \cdot 2 = 2^4$$

Continuing this logic, the number of grains on the 64th (and last) square will be 2^{64}, a massive number.

This scenario can be generalized with two slight modifications. First, instead of imagining growth occurring from square to square, imagine growth occurring as *time passes*. Then the powers can be viewed as elapsed time. Keeping with the rice example, beginning with 2 grains and doubling the quantity every day for 70 days would yield 2^{70} grains. The 2 is the growth rate and the power 70 represents the time that has elapsed.

Second, the growth rate does not have to be 2; in fact, it doesn't even have to be an integer. The rice analogy breaks down a bit at this point because a decimal growth rate requires fractional grains. However, we can easily substitute another analogy, like the growth of an invested dollar. For instance, growing a dollar for 5 days at a constant growth rate of 1.5 per day would produce an ending balance of $1.5^5 = 7.59$ dollars (rounded to the nearest penny). The key here is that we can choose *any* positive number as the growth rate, and apply it for *any* length of time by raising it to higher and higher powers.

It should be fairly predictable that any fixed growth rate larger than 1 will lead to never-ending growth. After all, from a mathematical perspective this entails nothing more than multiplying a number by itself over and over. On the contrary, growth rates between 0 and 1 will lead to decay. The study of decay is not our primary focus, but unsurprisingly, it will cause the quantity to shrink toward 0 as time passes.

There is one special case—what happens if the growth rate is exactly 1? Well, no growth *or* decay takes place, and the quantity remains static. The number 1 can be raised to any power and the result is still 1; think of 1 as the dividing line between growth and decay.

Now let's try to create a more realistic scenario. A tree doesn't suddenly double in size when the time is right. Instead, it grows a small amount every instant, combining a very small growth rate with very fast time periods.

Small growth rates imply numbers close to, but slightly larger than 1. To achieve this, we will use the convenient expression:

$$\left(1 + \frac{1}{n}\right)$$

As n grows, $\frac{1}{n}$ gets smaller, and the sum in parentheses becomes 1 plus a very small quantity. For $n = 100$ the growth rate is:

$$\left(1 + \frac{1}{100}\right) = 1.01$$

With this small growth rate, we can simulate "time passing" by increasing the power. The resulting numbers are rounded to one decimal place:

$$(1.01)^{10} = 1.1$$
$$(1.01)^{100} = 2.7$$
$$(1.01)^{1000} = 20959.2$$
$$(1.01)^{2000} = 439286205.0$$

Even with this modest growth rate, by the time the power reaches 2000 the result is already into the hundreds of millions. Computing higher powers will simply cause the quantity to grow without bound.

Let's choose a larger n to decrease the growth rate, $n = 1000$:

$$\left(1 + \frac{1}{1000}\right) = 1.001$$

As before, we will simulate the passage of time by raising the growth rate to higher and higher powers:

$$(1.001)^{100} = 1.1$$
$$(1.001)^{1000} = 2.7$$
$$(1.001)^{10000} = 21916.7$$
$$(1.001)^{20000} = 480340920.9$$

The powers are larger, but at 20000 the quantity is again starting to grow out of control. Even though the growth rate is small, there are still explosive gains after enough time has passed.

Unfortunately, no matter how close the growth rate is to 1, the resulting quantity will always grow beyond all bounds. The powers will need to be very high, but even an extremely small growth rate will eventually grow beyond control. Growth in the real world doesn't behave like this, so something more than just a very small growth rate is necessary.

The next idea will seem a little strange at first, but both the growth rate and the power will be chosen *at the same time*. This only requires a slight change to the previous expression. We will raise it to the power n:

$$\left(1 + \frac{1}{n}\right)^n$$

As an example, choosing $n = 100$ "applies the growth rate $(1 + \frac{1}{100}) = 1.01$ for 100 time periods". With a bit of imagination this can be related to the opening chessboard example. The growth rate for the grain of rice would be a paltry 1.01, and the "chessboard" would contain 100 squares. The expression:

$$\left(1 + \frac{1}{100}\right)^{100}$$

provides the quantity of rice on the last (100th) square (which comes out to about 2.70 grains). The delicate yet important detail here is that a tug of war between the growth rate and the time periods has now commenced. Choosing a large n will yield a *small* growth rate, but it will be applied for *more* time periods. It is not exactly clear what will happen as n grows.

Using multiples of 10 for simplicity and rounding to five decimal places, the results below show what happens as n is increased:

$$\left(1 + \frac{1}{10}\right)^{10} = 2.59374$$

$$\left(1 + \frac{1}{100}\right)^{100} = 2.70481$$

$$\left(1 + \frac{1}{1000}\right)^{1000} = 2.71692$$

$$\left(1 + \frac{1}{10000}\right)^{10000} = 2.71815$$

$$\left(1 + \frac{1}{100000}\right)^{100000} = 2.71827$$

This is certainly unexpected! The results do not grow without bound, but they do not decay either. Instead, the tug of war between the growth rate and the power pulls the expression toward a mysterious number approximately equal to 2.718.

In actuality, n can keep growing into the millions, billions, trillions, and beyond. The expression converges to a number known as *Euler's number* after the famous 18th-century Swiss mathematician Leonard Euler. This number is so famous that it even has its own symbol, e. It is approximately equal to:

$$e = 2.7182818284590452...$$

Like π, e is an irrational number, which means that its digits go on forever with no discernible repeating pattern (we'll study irrational numbers in a future letter). The number e represents what happens when *continuous compound growth* occurs.

We've found that the expression:

$$\left(1 + \frac{1}{n}\right)^{n}$$

converges to e as n increases. As a reminder, the $\left(1 + \frac{1}{n}\right)$ term represents the growth rate, and the power n represents the elapsed time periods. One natural interpretation of this expression is money growth in a bank account, and we can use this analogy to gain insight into the concept of continuous growth.

Suppose \$1 is deposited in a bank that promises 100% interest in one year. At the end of the year, the balance will be \$2, consisting of the original \$1 plus the interest payment of \$1.

Now suppose the bank offers the same deal, but will pay the 100% interest in *two* semi-annual installments of 50% each. After the first payment, the total will be \$1.50. Here is the important part: when the second payment is received at the end of the year, it will be paid on the *existing* balance. The existing balance is $1.50, so the second interest payment will be 50% of $1.50, which is $.75. Adding the final $.75 payment to the existing $1.50 balance gives a total of $2.25 at the end of the year. Notice that the total is $.25 more than if interest were only paid once per year.

What if the bank paid the same 100% interest 4 times a year in installments of 25% each? The first payment would bring the balance to $1.25. The next payment would be 25% of $1.25, which comes out to $.31 (rounded to the nearest penny). Adding this to the existing balance gives $1.25 + $.31 = $1.56. The third payment would be 25% of $1.56 to give a new balance of $1.95. The final payment would be 25% of $1.95, leaving a final balance of $2.44.

This interest growth scenario is precisely captured by the expression:

$$\left(1 + \frac{1}{n}\right)^n$$

If the 100% interest is paid 2 times a year, the ending balance is given by $n = 2$:

$$\left(1 + \frac{1}{2}\right)^2 = 2.25$$

If it is compounded 4 times a year, the ending balance is given by $n = 4$:

$$\left(1 + \frac{1}{4}\right)^4 = 2.44$$

This expression wraps the computation into a nice tidy package.

Lastly, what if the bank agreed to pay 100% interest in 365 equal *daily* installments, where a small amount of interest is calculated on the existing balance each day? How much money would there be at the end of the year? Rounding to the nearest penny the account total at the end of the year would be:

$$\left(1 + \frac{1}{365}\right)^{365} = 2.71$$

If the bank agreed to pay interest every hour or minute or second in equal installments, the ending balance would approach e dollars.

This analogy should help illuminate the concept of continuous growth, and it applies far beyond bank accounts. Most growth processes found in nature don't occur in sudden discrete steps, but in continuous tiny increments.

As you wade further into the world of mathematics you will start to notice how astoundingly interconnected it is. The number e shows up in so many unexpected places that it almost defies belief. It plays a central role in the fields of statistics, probability theory, trigonometry, and calculus to name a few. It even holds a heralded place in the field of complex analysis, which involves the use of so-called imaginary numbers.

Many mathematicians would argue that the following formula, known as *Euler's identity*, is the most beautiful relationship ever discovered:

$$e^{i \cdot \pi} + 1 = 0$$

The i is the famous *imaginary unit* defined as $i = \sqrt{-1}$. A full discussion of imaginary numbers is beyond the scope of this letter, but suffice it to say that there is a well-established way to deal with square roots of negative numbers. The expression above says that if we raise the number e to the power $\sqrt{-1} \cdot \pi$ and add 1, we get 0.

This is an instance where a full understanding of the formula requires a substantial background in mathematics. Nonetheless, you don't need to be a mathematician to appreciate the fact that so many famous and seemingly unrelated numbers, including e, i, π, 1, and 0 share a mysterious bond.

Fractals

Letter 7

Those who have learned to walk on the threshold of the unknown worlds, by means of what are commonly termed par excellence the exact sciences, may then, with the fair white wings of imagination, hope to soar further into the unexplored amidst which we live.
-Ada Lovelace

Fractals are one of the most extraordinary creations of modern mathematics. While properties of the infinitely complex shapes have been studied for at least a century, only with the advent of computers have we been able to visualize them. The mathematics of fractals matured in the 1970s with the work of the brilliant mathematician Benoit Mandelbrot. His influential publications brought these strange objects to the forefront of mainstream mathematics. To understand where fractals come from it is best to start with an example.

Consider an equilateral triangle.

Equilateral Triangle

Three simple geometric operations will be applied to it:

1. Shrink the sides to half their original length.
2. Make 3 copies.
3. Stack the 3 copies to make one larger triangle the same size as the original.

The first two steps are straightforward and lead to 3 identical triangles—each one with half the side length of the original.

Three Half Size Copies

The final step is to stack them into the shape of the original triangle:

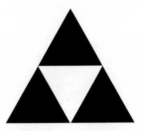

Three Half Size Copies Stacked

This composite triangle is exactly the same size and shape as the one we started with.

Now using *this* triangle, the process can be repeated. The first two steps yield three identical copies:

Three Half Size Copies

The last step (stacking) creates the new triangle shown below:

Three Half Size Copies Stacked

Once again, the new triangle is the same size and shape as the original.

This process can be continued indefinitely; shrink, copy, stack, and the steps can be applied to the resulting triangle once again.

What kind of object emerges if these steps are repeated many times? The first two iterations show that the shading of the composite triangle certainly changes. After the first application an upside-down white triangle appears in the center, and after the second, three smaller upside-down triangles surround the larger one in the center. Will the black shading eventually disappear? Or could the triangle end up completely shaded in black once again?

What actually happens is rather remarkable. The next image approximates the resulting triangle after repeating these operations many times, and is enlarged to show more detail. This famous fractal is known as the *Sierpiński triangle* after the Polish mathematician Wacław Sierpiński who described it in 1915.

Sierpiński Triangle

Notice the beautiful symmetry and *self-similarity* of the smaller sub-triangles—each one resembles the overall image. Focusing on any one of the 3 main sub-triangles again reveals even smaller triangles resembling the whole. Continued magnification will show that every composite triangle is a mini version of the overall image.

Applying the shrink, copy, stack steps yet again will produce virtually the same image. In a sense, the triangle has *converged* to an object that is impervious to the three steps. Recalling our study of chaos and feedback loops in a previous letter, this is the geometric equivalent of a feedback loop converging to a single point. This makes sense if the steps are viewed as a kind of geometric feedback loop. The output of one application of the rules is used as input for the next, and just as some feedback loops eventually converge to a single number, this geometric feedback loop eventually converges to a single shape.

Roughly speaking, a figure qualifies as a fractal if it displays aspects of infinite self-similarity. In other words, zooming into certain areas of a fractal will expose shapes that bear a close resemblance to the overall image. This isn't our first encounter with the concept of self-similarity. Similar curiosities surfaced in the feedback loop plots presented in a previous letter. Systems that produce fractals usually share a common trait; the repeated application of simple rules. The rules can take the form of a mathematical function, or a set of geometric operations.

Let's consider another example. The geometric operations will only affect the perimeter, but the starting shape will be an equilateral triangle as before:

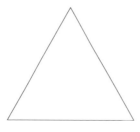

Equilateral Triangle

The rules are shown below, but they are easier to visualize than they are to read.

1. Divide each line segment into 3 pieces of equal length.
2. Remove the middle segment and replace it with a small equilateral triangle facing outward.
3. Remove the base of the small outward-facing triangle from step 2.

The triangle is made up of 3 line segments, and all three rules will be applied to each segment. An application to the bottom line segment of the triangle looks like this:

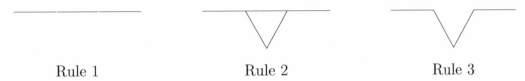

Rule 1   Rule 2   Rule 3

Applying the rules to all 3 line segments yields the figure below:

One Application of Rules

The outward-facing triangles from step 2 manifest as three "spikes" jutting out from the sides of the original triangle. Notice that these rules are different from the previous example in an important way. In this case, the rules apply to each line segment on the perimeter of the shape. In contrast, the shrink, copy, stack steps applied to the entire shape itself.

A second application of the rules is much more tedious, since they apply to each of the 12 line segments in the previous figure.

Two Applications of Rules

The outline of the original triangle is still vaguely visible, but the overall shape is beginning to resemble a star or a snowflake. Regardless of the emerging shape, the evolution of the original triangle can continue indefinitely. As before, our interest is in the long-term behavior of this shape as the rules are applied over and over. The eventual outcome is known as the *Koch snowflake*, named after Helge von Koch who discovered it in the early 1900s. This fractal is shown below and is enlarged to expose more detail.

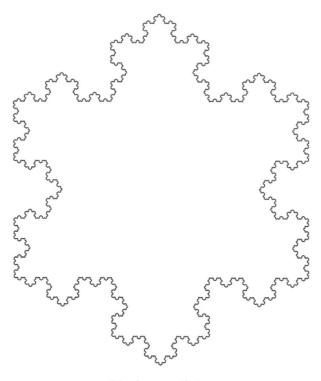

Koch snowflake

The self-similarity can be observed along the edges of the figure.

If the Koch snowflake or Sierpiński triangle were rendered on a computer with infinitely many pixels, self-similar patterns would come into focus at *every* zoom level. From a mathematical perspective, this infinite self-similarity is what makes fractals so special. It is worthwhile to note that any picture of a fractal is only an approximation, because the capability to zoom is limited by the size of a single pixel on a computer or the smallest ink droplet on a printed page. Mathematically accurate representations of fractals contain *infinite* detail, and can therefore only be imagined. That being said, these pictures provide enough detail to give a sense of what fractals look like.

As demonstrated above, one way to discover fractals is to invent a set of geometric rules, apply them repeatedly, and hope that a fractal emerges. However, there is an astonishing alternative known as the *chaos game*. It is an iterative process of plotting points that eventually merge into an image. The name is related to the fact that the points are drawn in a somewhat chaotic manner; but the rules for rendering the points can be quite simple. Similar to our previous study of Conway's Game of Life, the word *game* is used rather loosely. In reality, it is simply a methodical process that progresses the system toward the final image.

The chaos game does not consist of a single set of rules, but offers a framework in which parameters can be altered to achieve different outcomes. The first step is to choose a handful of initial "base" points. Then a set of probabilistic rules are applied to plot points around and in between the base points.

Below is an example that starts with 3 base points arranged in the shape of an equilateral triangle. For reference, the three points are labelled 1, 2, and 3.

3

1   2

Three Points Forming a Triangle

A randomly chosen point inside the triangle begins the game. For clarity, the point will be drawn on the edge of the triangle between base points 1 and 2.

3

1   .   2

The First Point

The game is progressed by applying the following rules:

1. Randomly select one of the 3 base points.
2. Move half the distance from the current point to the selected base point, and draw a point.
3. The new point becomes the current point. Repeat from step 1.

The random point drawn between base points 1 and 2 is considered the first "current" point. The next step is to randomly choose one of the three base points. For the sake of demonstration, let's select base point 3. We'll move half the distance from the current point to the selected base point. Lastly, a point is drawn at this halfway mark as shown next:

3
.

.

.
1   .   .
                                                             2

The Second Point

The new point becomes the current point and the steps repeat. Suppose we randomly select base point 1 this time. Now another point is drawn half the distance between the current point and base point 1:

3
.

.

.

.
1   .   .
                                                             2

The Third Point

This becomes the current point and the steps repeat.

So what happens if we continue drawing points according to these rules? Will the triangle fill in with black dots until it appears solid? Intuition suggests that since the base point selection is random, the final image will be messy.

The actual pattern that emerges is almost unbelievable. The three plots below represent the results of progressing the game through 100, 1000, and 25000 iterations.

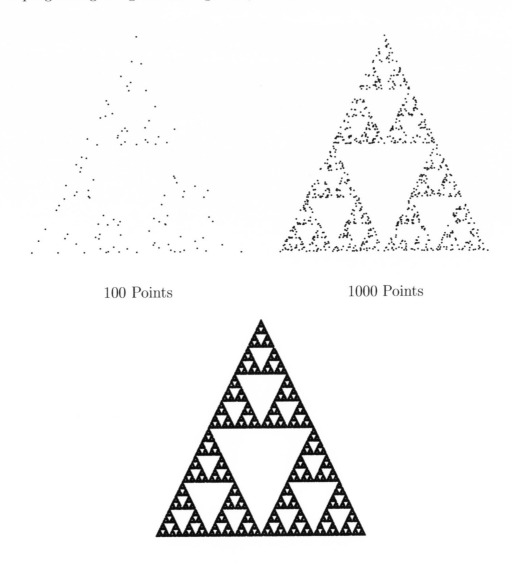

100 Points

1000 Points

25000 Points

The points coalesce into a unified image, and as if by magic, the Sierpiński triangle appears! It turns out that no matter where inside the triangle the very first point is drawn, and no matter the sequence of random base point selections, the Sierpiński triangle will *always* emerge. The only caveat is that there may be a few stray points depending on where the first one was chosen.

The chaos game can be leveraged to generate many interesting fractals. The rules laid out above give only one example; slight changes will create new images. For instance, altering step 2 to rotate by 7.5 degrees before moving toward the randomly selected base point results in the following image.

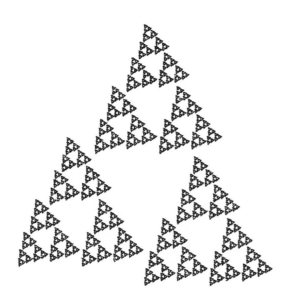

Chaos Game with Slightly Different Rules

Increasing the number of base points is also an option. Let's try starting with 6 base points in the shape of a hexagon. The rules will remain almost the same as before, but instead of moving half the distance to a randomly chosen base point, we'll move $\frac{2}{3}$ the distance. After 60000 iterations the image below emerges:

Chaos Game with 6 Vertices and Modified Rules

Note that the outline of the Koch snowflake materializes in the center. It is not uncommon to find fractals hidden within other fractals.

Believe it or not, the next image was produced using the chaos game methodology with four specialized rules. Unfortunately, writing the rules out isn't particularly easy, because they can only be expressed succinctly using mathematical functions. The functions are not overly complex, but reviewing them would lead us too far astray (they require some familiarity with *linear algebra*). Here is the final image after 25000 points are drawn:

Chaos Game with Special Rules

It is rather astounding, but as this image shows, some fractals have the curious ability to mimic organic structures like ferns or leaves.

The fractals shown here are only a small sampling of the many images mathematicians have discovered over the years. A common trait nearly all fractals share is that they arise from rules applied over and over. This fact echoes a theme from previous letters: complex objects and processes are not necessarily governed by equally complex rules. We'll revisit fractals in a future letter, and some exceptionally stunning specimens will be explored.

Irrational Numbers

Letter 8

Mathematics seems to endow one with something like a new sense.
-Charles Darwin

Solving practical problems like measuring boards for a bookshelf, making change for a customer, or tallying points in a basketball game rarely call for anything more sophisticated than integers and standard fractions. These numbers all fall into the realm of *rational* numbers, which means that they can be expressed as the ratio of two integers (hence the term *ratio*nal). There exists, however, a large world of *irrational* numbers, simply defined as any number that is not rational. In a sense, there are actually *more* irrational numbers than there are rational ones. Despite their abundance, irrational numbers have some peculiar properties.

All integers are rational since each can trivially be written as itself over 1 (e.g. $5 = \frac{5}{1}$). It is self-evident that all common fractions are rational as well—numbers like $\frac{1}{16}$, $\frac{3}{8}$, and $\frac{1}{2}$ fit the definition of integer ratios. The fact of the matter is that nearly all numbers used in daily life are rational.

How about numbers like .333... where the 3 repeats forever, or a number like .123123... where a sequence of numbers (in this case 123) repeats forever? What about a randomly chosen decimal number like 2.5678? It turns out that any number that can be written in decimal format with either a finite number of digits, or digits that eventually repeat in some pattern, is rational. This can be proven with a trick that converts these decimal numbers into a ratio of integers.

To begin, recall that multiplying a decimal number by 10 moves the decimal point one place to the right; for example $10 \cdot .123123... = 1.23123...$. We'll use this fact to show that .123123... can be written as a ratio of integers.

The key is to keep multiplying .123123... by 10 until the digits to the right of the decimal point are the same as in the original number. In this case, we need to multiply by three copies of 10 or $10 \cdot 10 \cdot 10 = 1000$:

$$1000 \cdot .123123... = 123.123123...$$

Notice that the digits after the decimal point on the right side of the equation are exactly the same as the original number .123123.... Remember, the pattern of 123 goes on forever, so although multiplication by 1000 moves the decimal point three places to the right, there are still infinitely many copies of 123 after the decimal point.

Now take the equality above and subtract the original number .123123... from both sides:

$$1000 \cdot .123123... - .123123... = 123.123123... - .123123...$$

Let's focus on the right side of this equation for a moment. The interesting conclusion here is that all the numbers beyond the decimal point cancel out. This is easier to see if the subtraction is written like this:

$$
\begin{array}{r}
123.123123... \\
- \quad .123123... \\
\hline
123.000000...
\end{array}
$$

The integer 123 is all that remains on the right side:

$$1000 \cdot .123123... - .123123... = 123$$

On the left side, the rules of multiplication allow for a common factor of .123123... to be "pulled out" of the subtraction. The expression:

$$1000 \cdot .123123... - .123123...$$

Is the same as:

$$(1000 - 1) \cdot .123123...$$

$(1000 - 1) = 999$ so the previous expression can be simplified to:

$$999 \cdot .123123...$$

Therefore, the left side of the equation:

$$1000 \cdot .123123... - .123123... = 123$$

can be written as:

$$999 \cdot .123123... = 123$$

The final step is to divide both sides by 999. This will cancel the 999 on the left side since $\frac{999}{999} = 1$ and only the original number .123123... will be left:

$$.123123... = \frac{123}{999}$$

This result can be checked by dividing 123 by 999 on a calculator.

A technique similar to the one above can be used to write any arbitrary decimal number as a ratio of integers. The only restriction is that the digits to the right of the decimal point must *eventually* repeat in some pattern forever. For numbers with finitely many digits, like 2.5678, the approach is even simpler because no equations are necessary. Dividing by 10 moves the decimal point one place to the left, so if the number 25678 (or 25678.0 if the decimal point is included) is divided by 10 four times (or $10 \cdot 10 \cdot 10 \cdot 10 = 10000$) it will become 2.5678. Therefore, 2.5678 can be written as the ratio of integers 25678 and 10000:

$$2.5678 = \frac{25678}{10000}$$

These examples should convince you that rational numbers are ubiquitous and that nearly every number encountered in our daily lives is rational.

Now we can move on to *irrational* numbers. Can you think of an example? Unless you happen to remember one from school, this may be a struggle. As a matter of fact, irrational numbers can't even be written down in the traditional sense—mathematicians had to invent symbols to represent them.

The most famous irrational number is undoubtedly π, the area of a circle with radius 1, and is approximately equal to 3.14159. The word *approximately* is important here. The oddity of irrational numbers is that their digits not only go on forever, they go on forever with *no discernible repeating pattern*. When irrational numbers are used in real-world applications there is no choice but to approximate them with computers.

By definition, π cannot be written as a ratio of two integers. We can get close, for instance, $\frac{22}{7} = 3.142857142857...$ (note the repeating pattern), but there are no two integers, no matter how large, whose ratio is exactly equal to π.

Another example can be derived using the Pythagorean theorem, which ensures that the legs of a right triangle always satisfy the relation $a^2 + b^2 = c^2$. If a right triangle has sides $a = 1$ and $b = 1$:

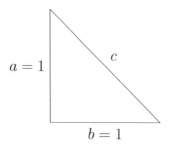

then the length of the third side c must satisfy:

$$1^2 + 1^2 = c^2$$

which leads to:

$$2 = c^2$$

The length c is a number such that, when it is squared, yields 2.

What number is that? Well, $1^2 = 1$ is too small, and $2^2 = 4$ is too big; so the number c must be between 1 and 2. Let's try 1.5:

$$1.5^2 = 2.25$$

Too big. Let's try 1.4:

$$1.4^2 = 1.960$$

This is closer, but still too small. Increasing the number slightly to 1.41 gives:

$$1.41^2 = 1.988$$

We're getting closer to the length c, but guessing numbers is tedious work. Luckily, mathematicians invented the *square root* symbol. Writing $\sqrt{2}$ is shorthand for "the number such that when squared yields 2", thus the answer is:

$$\sqrt{2} = c$$

The number $\sqrt{2}$ happens to be irrational. Guessing numbers and squaring them to hit 2 would never work—we would need to guess a number with infinitely many digits possessing no apparent pattern. The first several digits of $\sqrt{2}$ are:

$$1.414213562373...$$

As implied earlier, when trailing dots are written after a number like .123123... it means that the pattern 123 continues on forever. However, when there is no apparent pattern in the digits, the trailing dots imply infinite continuation without structure.

The two examples above are based on real-world geometric concepts, and demonstrate that irrational numbers are not simply an elaborate mathematical construct with no basis in reality. Irrational numbers are not difficult to find, and in fact the square root of any integer that is not a perfect square will be irrational. The numbers $\sqrt{3}, \sqrt{5}, \sqrt{6}, \sqrt{7}$ and so on are all irrational.

Can a number be neither rational nor irrational? In other words, are there real numbers outside of these two sets? The answer is no—combining the rationals and irrationals completes our real number system.

Given that they do not occur often in real life, perhaps one of the most surprising facts about irrational numbers is that there are so many of them. There are infinitely many rational numbers (the integers alone go on forever), and there are also infinitely many irrational numbers. The strange truth is that there are, in a sense, "more" irrational numbers than rational ones. Different concepts of infinity will be discussed in a future letter, but the following gives a preview: the size of the set of all irrational numbers is a different kind of infinity, known as *uncountable infinity*. This kind of infinity is a distinctly larger class when compared to the infinity of the rationals.

Let's turn our focus to the digits of an irrational number. Here are the beginning digits of $\sqrt{2}$:

1.41421356237309504880168872420969807856967187537694807317667973799073247846210703885038753432764157273501384623091229702492483605585073721264412149709993583141322266592750559275579995050115278206057147010955997160597027453459686201472851741

And here are the beginning digits for π:

3.14159265358979323846264338327950288419716939937510582097494459230781640628620899862803482534211706798214808651328230664709384460955058223172535940812848111745028410270193852110555964462294895493038196442881097566593344612847564823378678311

Scanning these digits is rather daunting, and this is only the slightest peek. It's hard to imagine that the digits go on forever in a seemingly random manner, but they do.

This raises another question—are the digits uniformly distributed? Namely, do the digits 0 through 9 all occur with equal frequency, or do some show up more often than others? Could a digit stop appearing after a certain point?

One way to approach this problem is through empirical tests. We can count how many times each digit appears and see if there is a substantial difference in the counts. If large differences appear then perhaps the irrational number favors some digits over others.

The problem of course, is that the digits go on forever, so choosing a reasonable stopping point for the experiment is necessary. Let's start with the first 1000 digits and see what happens. The bar charts below show the frequency of each digit for π and $\sqrt{2}$, and the dashed line shows where the bars would be if all digits appeared equally:

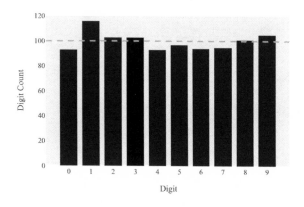

First 1000 Digits of π First 1000 Digits of $\sqrt{2}$

There are a few visible differences between counts; for instance, 1 seems to be more prevalent in π and 8 in $\sqrt{2}$.

Increasing the number of digits to 100000 gives smoother bars:

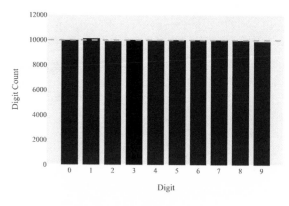 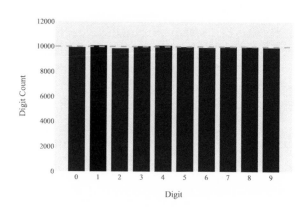

First 100000 Digits of π First 100000 Digits of $\sqrt{2}$

The bars are now almost exactly level across the top, just touching the dashed line.

From these tests and others like it (using trillions of digits) it appears that the digits of π and $\sqrt{2}$ are equally distributed. However, despite significant effort, no one has been able to *prove* that this is the case. It is still unknown if the digits in the infinite tails of these numbers continue on with the same frequency forever. This is rather amazing considering the prominence of the number π, and to a lesser extent, $\sqrt{2}$.

Not all irrational numbers are completely devoid of obvious patterns. Suppose we form the never ending decimal number .123456789101112131415... by concatenating the successive positive integers. This is an irrational number, but unlike π and $\sqrt{2}$, it has been proven that the digits 0 through 9 appear with equal frequency. It has also been shown that every possible finite string of digits must appear somewhere in this number. In other words, your birthday, your phone number, and any other digit combination you can think of are all encoded in this number. For that matter, the same is true for everyone on the planet. This might not come as a complete surprise since it was constructed artificially, but these types of numbers do exist.

Are you guaranteed to find your birthday, phone number, and any other arbitrary string of digits somewhere in π, $\sqrt{2}$, or e? It is widely believed that the answer is yes, but no one has been able to prove it.

Adding to the intrigue of irrational numbers is the fact that they are not "closed" under addition, which means that summing two irrational numbers does not necessarily result in another irrational number. The rational numbers, on the other hand, are closed under addition—adding together two rationals always results in another rational. In contrast, adding together two irrational numbers can result in a rational *or* irrational number, and in some cases the irrationality of a sum is not known. For example, take the famous irrational number e encountered in a previous letter on continuous growth, and add it to π:

$$\pi + e = ?$$

The resulting sum is a number close to 5.8, but although much is known about both e and π, it is *unknown* whether or not their sum is irrational. This highlights a core difficulty with irrational numbers; while they are plentiful, it is not always straightforward to prove irrationality.

Practically speaking, irrational numbers are easily rounded to a nearby rational number prior to use in an actual application. It is hard to imagine an engineering computation where rounding π to 20 decimal places would not suffice. Be that as it may, irrational numbers are astounding objects in their own right, and their properties will continue to intrigue mathematicians for generations to come.

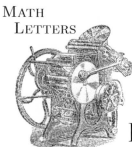

Fibonacci & the Golden Rectangle

Letter 9

The great book of nature is written in mathematics.
-Galileo

There are instances where the elegant proportions of an object appear naturally pleasing to the eye. One example of this, whose origins date back to the ancient Greeks, is the *golden rectangle*. Although it is no more than a simple geometric shape, it has appeared time and again in works of art and architecture.

Unlike many objects of beauty, this one adheres to a particular mathematical principle. To derive the golden rectangle, we will start with a square of side length 1:

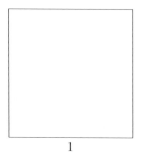

Square with Side Length 1

The goal is to turn this square into a golden rectangle, but it is not yet clear how far the sides should be extended. For now, the symbol x will act as a placeholder, and a hypothetical dotted-line will extend the square. The final rectangle will consist of the square plus the dotted region:

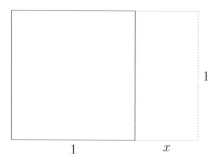

Extending Square by Length x

The only remaining problem is how to choose the length x.

To illustrate a concrete example, let's randomly chose x to be .3, so that the long side measures $1 + .3 = 1.3$.

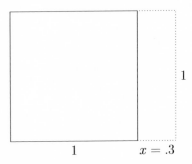

Extending Square by Length .3

To construct the golden rectangle the value of x must be more precise—it won't be an arbitrary number. Instead, x will need to satisfy a very specific *self-similarity* property. Our previous letter on fractals showed that self-similar shapes generally exhibit pleasing symmetries. Luckily, the self-similarity property imposed here will be relatively simple.

Notice that in the picture above, the dotted-line area actually forms a second smaller rectangle within the larger one. The large rectangle has long side length $1 + x$ (1.3 in this example), and short side length 1. Meanwhile, the small dotted-line rectangle has long side length 1 and short side length x (.3 in this example). The self-similarity property we'll impose is as follows: choose x in such a way that the small rectangle is *similar* to the large rectangle.

What does it mean for two rectangles to be similar? Two rectangles are considered similar if the ratios formed by their long and short sides are equal. For example, a rectangle with long side 10 and short side 5 is similar to a rectangle with long side 8 and short side 4. Although they differ in size, the ratio formed by the sides of the first $\frac{10}{5} = 2$ is equal to the ratio formed by the sides of the second $\frac{8}{4} = 2$.

With the picture above in mind, this can be expressed in terms of x. The long side of the large rectangle is $1 + x$ and the short side is 1, so the ratio of sides is $\frac{1+x}{1}$. The small rectangle has long side 1 and short side x, so the ratio of sides is $\frac{1}{x}$. Now set these two ratios equal to one another:

$$\frac{1 + x}{1} = \frac{1}{x}$$

Take a moment to compare this algebraic statement to the pictures. We're merely forming the ratio $\frac{\text{long side}}{\text{short side}}$ for both rectangles and setting them equal to one another.

Now the challenge is to find the positive number x which satisfies this expression. Fortunately, we can use a little algebra and a well-known formula to find a solution.

First, multiply both sides by x:

$$x \cdot \left(\frac{1 + x}{1}\right) = x \cdot \left(\frac{1}{x}\right)$$

The right side can be written more simply as $\frac{x}{x}$ after multiplying x by the 1 in the numerator. Dividing any number by itself always yields 1, so the right side simplifies to $\frac{x}{x} = 1$.

$$x \cdot \left(\frac{1 + x}{1} \right) = 1$$

On the left side, the distributive property of multiplication can be applied to multiply the x across the parentheses.

$$\left(\frac{x \cdot 1 + x \cdot x}{1} \right) = 1$$

The 1 in the denominator on the left side is redundant and can be dropped. Let's also write $x \cdot 1$ as x since multiplication by 1 does not change x. Finally, $x \cdot x$ is the same as x^2. After these simplifications the equation becomes:

$$x + x^2 = 1$$

We'll rearrange this slightly by letting x^2 be the first term and subtracting 1 from both sides, leaving the right side with $1 - 1 = 0$:

$$x^2 + x - 1 = 0$$

Solutions for this equation can be found using the *quadratic formula*—typically introduced in middle school. Remember, all we've done is manipulate the expression into a different format, and this strategy is quite common in mathematics. If an expression can be manipulated into a well-known form, then a preexisting formula can usually be used to solve it. We won't write the quadratic formula in its entirety, as it will add little insight to our discussion. Its only purpose is to provide a mechanical way to arrive at a solution for this equation.

It turns out that the solution is given by the irrational number:

$$\frac{\sqrt{5} - 1}{2} = .618033...$$

As with all irrational numbers, the digits go on forever with no discernible repeating pattern.

To verify, this number can be plugged into both sides of the original expression to check that they are equal:

$$\frac{1 + x}{1} = \frac{1}{x}$$

Plugging in on the left side and using a calculator gives:

$$\frac{1 + \left(\frac{\sqrt{5} - 1}{2} \right)}{1} = 1.618033...$$

And on the right:

$$\frac{1}{\left(\frac{\sqrt{5} - 1}{2} \right)} = 1.618033...$$

So this is indeed the correct choice of x. Furthermore, this is the *only* positive x that works.

The solution $x = .618033...$ is the magic number that will turn our square into a golden rectangle:

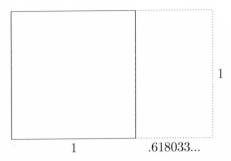

Golden Rectangle Construction

Now that the proper side extension x has been determined, we can draw the golden rectangle by itself without the dotted-line:

Golden Rectangle

Any rectangle with the ratio $\frac{\text{long side}}{\text{short side}} = 1.618033...$ is a golden rectangle, and the irrational number $1.618033...$ is aptly named the *golden ratio*. As with other famous irrational numbers like π and e, the golden ratio has a symbol associated with it, the Greek letter phi:

$$\phi = \frac{1 + \sqrt{5}}{2} = 1.618033...$$

Although subject to some debate, the golden rectangle and the related golden ratio have been observed in architecture dating back to the ancient Greek Parthenon. Some even claim that the golden ratio can be observed in earlier structures such as the Great Pyramid of Giza. Regardless of its use (deliberate or accidental) in architecture, the golden rectangle and golden ratio have been known since antiquity. Golden rectangles have many properties worth exploring, and we will briefly discuss two of particular interest.

Consider the Golden Rectangle Construction diagram from above. Is the smaller rectangle outlined by the dotted-line also a golden rectangle? It has long side 1 and short side $.618033...$ So the ratio of sides is:

$$\frac{1}{.618033...} = 1.618033...$$

Since the ratio of sides is equal to the golden ratio, the smaller rectangle is indeed a golden rectangle. Notice the peculiar result of the division—dividing 1 by .618033... simply "adds 1" to .618033...

It is a little surprising what happens when the smaller rectangle is divided into a square piece and an even smaller rectangle, in essence, mimicking the construction of the larger rectangle. We'll draw a dashed line in the small rectangle to create a square on the bottom, and another little rectangle on top.

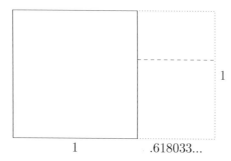

Spawning Another Golden Rectangle

Believe it or not, the small rectangle in the upper right is again a golden rectangle.

It doesn't end there. Splitting this new rectangle into a square and an even smaller rectangle produces the following:

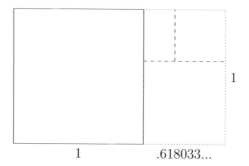

Spawning Another Golden Rectangle

The small interior rectangle is again a golden rectangle.

This process can continue indefinitely. Each time the new rectangle is split into a perfect square and another smaller rectangle, the remaining rectangle is *always* a golden rectangle. This strange attribute is a manifestation of the self-similarity property imposed earlier. The golden rectangle is the only such rectangle where this is possible.

This infinite subdivision leads to another curious geometric object closely related to the golden ratio. As the large rectangle is subdivided into smaller and smaller interior golden rectangles, a series of contracting squares appear, three of which materialize in the figure above. If this process is continued, and a quarter circle arc is drawn within each square, the resulting image closely approximates the *golden spiral*.

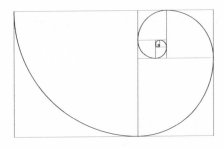

Golden Spiral

Like the golden ratio, it is claimed that the golden spiral represents a pervasive pattern in nature. For instance, the arrangement of seeds in a sunflower, the spiral scales on a pinecone, or certain seashells.

Geometry, however, isn't the only area where the golden ratio appears. As with many famous numbers in mathematics, the golden ratio tends to pop up in unexpected places. One remarkable instance is the Fibonacci sequence, first popularized by an Italian mathematician of the same name in the early 13th century. The sequence was originally meant to calculate the growth of an idealized (but by no means realistic) rabbit population. The first two numbers of the sequence are 1 and 1. To generate the next term, simply add together the previous two terms. Here is the start of the sequence:

$$1, 1, 2, 3, 5, 8, 13, 21, 34, 55, 89, \ldots$$

The next term would be $55 + 89 = 144$.

The Fibonacci sequence has been studied for hundreds of years and curiously appears in many different branches of mathematics; it also happens to share a link with the golden ratio. Let's investigate the *ratio* of successive Fibonacci numbers:

$$\frac{1}{1}, \frac{2}{1}, \frac{3}{2}, \frac{5}{3}, \frac{8}{5}, \frac{13}{8}, \frac{21}{13}, \frac{34}{21}, \frac{55}{34}, \frac{89}{55}, \ldots$$

Writing these fractions in decimal format and rounding to 4 decimal places produces the following sequence:

$$1, 2, 1.5, 1.6667, 1.6, 1.625, 1.6154, 1.6190, 1.6176, 1.6182, \ldots$$

The last number is suspiciously close to the golden ratio 1.618033...

In fact, the ratio of successive Fibonacci numbers converges *exactly* to the golden ratio as the sequence advances. The ratio of the 28th to 27th Fibonacci number rounded to four decimal places is $\frac{317811}{196418} = 1.6180$, which is already quite close to the golden ratio. This also implies that building a rectangle with side lengths equal to two successive Fibonacci numbers will closely approximate a golden rectangle.

There is an extraordinary formula that displays this close relationship between the golden ratio and the Fibonacci numbers. It is known as *Binet's formula* after the 19th century French mathematician Jacques Philippe Marie Binet, and it can be used to generate the nth Fibonacci number:

$$\frac{\phi^n - \left(\frac{-1}{\phi}\right)^n}{\sqrt{5}}$$

If we replace ϕ with the golden ratio and simplify we get:

$$\frac{(1 + \sqrt{5})^n - (1 - \sqrt{5})^n}{2^n \sqrt{5}}$$

To find, for example, the 10th Fibonacci number, replace n with 10:

$$\frac{(1 + \sqrt{5})^{10} - (1 - \sqrt{5})^{10}}{2^{10} \sqrt{5}} = 55$$

It is remarkable that the irrational numbers in this formula combine and cancel in just the right way to yield an integer.

The driving intellectual force behind much of pure mathematical research is the quest to uncover connections between diverse concepts. Discoveries like Binet's formula, linking the golden ratio to the Fibonacci numbers, is a prime example of the mysterious bond that permeates mathematics. Mathematicians are always searching for the next unexpected connection, slowly revealing the secret patterns that lurk just beneath the surface.

As we hinted earlier, there is some debate around the true pervasiveness of the golden rectangle, spiral, and ratio in architecture, art, and nature. There are entire books devoted to the subject. The counterargument is that it is easy to verify arbitrary patterns when choosing from thousands of examples. There is also some leeway in deciding how close a ratio needs to be in order to qualify. If the granite blocks of a building have a long to short side ratio of 1.6—can these be counted as golden rectangles? After all, the golden ratio is an irrational number, and can never be represented precisely in the real world. That being said, the golden ratio certainly arises more often than one would expect. Regardless of its true prevalence, the golden ratio and associated geometric structures have long captivated mathematicians and artists alike.

Prime Numbers

Letter 10

Mathematicians have tried in vain to this day to discover some order in the sequence of prime numbers, and we have reason to believe that it is a mystery into which the human mind will never penetrate.
—Leonhard Euler

Prime numbers have held a coveted place in the world of mathematics for centuries. As we will see, this is partly because they act as the fundamental building blocks for all integers. They also possess an uncanny ability to assert themselves across nearly every branch of mathematics. Despite their fame, the primes still hold many mysteries that mathematicians have been unable to crack.

A prime number is a positive integer larger than 1 that is only divisible by 1 and itself. There is one quick clarification to mention about this definition. When we say *divisible* we mean *evenly* divisible—that is, the result of the division is an integer. For example, the number 10 is evenly divisible by 5 since the answer is the integer 2. However, 10 is not evenly divisible by 4 since the answer is the decimal number 2.5. Throughout this letter, the term *divisible* will always imply even divisibility.

The first five primes are 2, 3, 5, 7, and 11. None of these integers have a divisor other than 1 and themselves. Non-prime numbers like 4, 6, 8, 9, and 10 are divisible by something other than 1 and themselves; 4 is divisible by 2, 9 is divisible by 3, and 6 is divisible by both 2 and 3. As you can see, the definition of a prime number is not overly complicated; their influence in mathematics primarily stems from the remarkable theorem discussed next.

The *Fundamental Theorem of Arithmetic* states:

> *Every* integer is either a prime number or can be represented as the unique product of prime numbers.

What does this mean exactly? Well, pick any integer. Let's use 15. The theorem states that either 15 is prime, or it can be written as a unique product of primes. The number 15 is not prime because it is at least divisible by 3. However, it can be written as a product of primes, $15 = 3 \cdot 5$.

The fact that *every* integer can be written as the product of primes, or is prime itself, is nearly unbelievable. Next, and this is a bit more subtle, the theorem states that the prime factorization is unique. In other words, there is only *one* way to write an integer as the product of primes.

Let's consider another example, say 24. We know that 24 is not prime, and there are many ways to write it as a product of other integers. For instance:

$$24 = 4 \cdot 6$$
$$24 = 2 \cdot 12$$
$$24 = 2 \cdot 2 \cdot 6$$

Nonetheless, there is only *one* factorization where all the numbers in the product are prime:

$$24 = 2 \cdot 2 \cdot 2 \cdot 3$$

Primes may be repeated in the product as they are here, but there is no other way to arrive at 24 as a product of prime numbers. It *must* be three 2s and one 3.

Decomposing an integer into its prime factors yields its *prime decomposition*. If the number is prime then it cannot be decomposed and the only factor it has is itself. Here are a few others:

$$8 = 2 \cdot 2 \cdot 2$$
$$10 = 2 \cdot 5$$
$$17 = 17$$
$$21 = 3 \cdot 7$$
$$25 = 5 \cdot 5$$
$$60 = 2 \cdot 2 \cdot 3 \cdot 5$$
$$100 = 2 \cdot 2 \cdot 5 \cdot 5$$
$$360 = 2 \cdot 2 \cdot 2 \cdot 3 \cdot 3 \cdot 5$$

This is why prime numbers are so important. Not only are they the building blocks of all integers, but they create a unique fingerprint for each.

It is easy to calculate every possible divisor for an integer once we know its prime decomposition. For example, 60 is divisible by each of its prime factors, and it is also divisible by all possible products of these factors such as $2 \cdot 3 \cdot 5 = 30$. Excluding 1 and itself, 60 is evenly divisible by:

$$2, 3, 4, 5, 6, 10, 12, 15, 20, 30$$

It turns out that 60 has more divisors than any integer below it. The same is true for 24 and 360. These numbers are on the other end of the spectrum from primes, and are sometimes called *anti-primes*, or more traditionally, *highly composite* numbers. One consequence of having so many divisors is that they can easily be split apart into halves, thirds, quarters and so on without worrying about fractional parts. This is one reason why we have 24 hours in a day, 60 minutes in an hour, and 360 degrees in a circle.

So far we've discussed the definition of a prime number, and why they are special, but only the first few prime numbers have been used as examples. It is fairly easy to test if a small integer is prime—but what about larger numbers? For that matter, *is* there a largest prime? This leads to two specific questions: How many prime numbers are there? And how can we easily determine if a given number is prime?

Is 12 prime? No, because it is divisible by something other than 1 and itself; the numbers 2, 3, 4, and 6 all divide 12. What about 13? This can be answered by cycling through each of the integers less than 13 and checking if any one of them is a divisor. In this case, every number fails the test, and so 13 must be prime.

Even with a calculator, this method of checking whether a number is prime or not isn't efficient. Is there a known formula that generates all primes? After all, there are formulas for other types of numbers like square numbers and the triangular numbers we encountered in a previous letter.

Unfortunately, there is no known formula to generate all primes. In fact, checking to see if an especially large number is prime isn't an easy task. There are ways to do it, but it is time-consuming and almost always requires the aid of a computer.

If there is no formula to generate prime numbers, how do we know how many exist? As the numbers grow, there are more divisors to try, and therefore a greater chance to *not* be prime. Checking the number 100000001 requires testing thousands of divisors, and the chance of at least *one* of them working seems fairly high. Do the prime numbers simply end at some point?

This brings us to another famous theorem which asserts that there are in fact *infinitely* many prime numbers. Considering what was mentioned above, this is quite extraordinary. For example, the number 2147483647 is prime, which implies that of the millions of divisors available, not a single one will work. The theorem ensures the existence of massive integers which, despite having billions of possible divisors, are still only divisible by 1 and themselves. Mathematicians are always on the hunt to discover ever-larger primes. The largest known prime number can potentially change any day. With the advent of computers, the largest known prime is tens of millions of *digits* long.

It is insightful to study the general approach of proving that there are infinitely many primes. A mathematical *proof* is a logical argument demonstrating why a particular claim is true, and behind every mathematical result, formula, and theorem is a proof showing its validity.

We start by assuming that there are *not* infinitely many primes, then the proof goes on to show that this cannot possibly be true. This is a common strategy known as *proof by contradiction*. The idea is to assume that the opposite is true, and then show that this eventually leads to an inconsistency. If an inconsistency is reached, then the alternative must be true. In this case, the alternative is there are infinitely many primes.

If there really *are* finitely many primes, then they can be arranged in a list. To avoid the hassle of writing actual numbers we will use placeholders like $p_1, p_2, p_3, ..., p_n$. The first symbol p_1 can be thought of as the first prime number 2, p_2 as the second prime number 3, p_3 as the third prime number 5, and so on all the way to the last (and largest) prime number p_n. The little subscript n is used because we do not presume to know exactly how many primes there are, just that they end at some point; n could be one hundred or it could be one million.

The trick is to form a special number, which we will call M, by multiplying the entire list of primes together and then adding 1. This construction will be explained in a moment:

$$M = p_1 \cdot p_2 \cdot p_3 \cdot ... \cdot p_n + 1$$

The expression above may look intimidating, but it is only an abstraction of simple arithmetic; $p_1 \cdot p_2 \cdot p_3 \cdot ... \cdot p_n$ are all the numbers in the list multiplied together. Remember, the symbols p_1 through p_n are just placeholders for actual numbers. The ellipsis stands in for the remaining primes between p_3 and p_n, where p_n signifies the largest number in the list. To give a concrete example, think of the product $p_1 \cdot p_2 \cdot p_3$ as $2 \cdot 3 \cdot 5$ consisting of the first 3 prime numbers. After multiplying all the primes in the list together the integer 1 is added to obtain the final number we've named M.

One thing we can immediately conclude about M is that it is not in the list of primes. This is because M is bigger than p_n, the largest prime in the list. The easiest way to see this is to note that the product of positive integers will always be larger than any single term used in the multiplication. For instance, $2 \cdot 3 \cdot 5 = 30$, and 30 is larger than 2, 3, or 5. Therefore, the product $p_1 \cdot p_2 \cdot p_3 \cdot ... \cdot p_n$ will be larger than any of its components, including p_n. Even before adding 1 to M, it is already larger than p_n, and so it cannot be in the list of primes.

Now, we are assuming that the list contains *all* primes, and we've also just shown that M cannot be in this list. Therefore, we can conclude that M is not a prime number.

There is one other thing we can deduce about M; it is not divisible by any prime in the list. The following example will illustrate why this is the case. Consider the product:

$$4 \cdot 5 \cdot 6 = 120$$

The number 120 is divisible by every term in the product: 4, 5, and 6. Now add 1 to the product to get:

$$4 \cdot 5 \cdot 6 + 1 = 121$$

The resulting number, 121, isn't divisible by *any* terms in the product. Attempting to divide 121 by 4, 5, or 6 will always leave a remainder of 1. As another example, 6 is divisible by both 2 and 3. Add 1 to 6 to get 7 and it is no longer divisible by 2 or 3. Adding 1 to a product will render the resulting number indivisible by any factor in that product.

This same logic applies to the number M. It was formed by adding 1 to the product of all primes, so attempting to divide M by any one of them will always leave a remainder of 1. Consequently, M is not divisible by any prime in the list.

The last detail is to notice that for any number, every number in its prime decomposition will evenly divide it. For example, $10 = 2 \cdot 5$ and both 2 and 5 evenly divide 10.

To recap, we've established that:

1. M is not a prime number.

2. None of the primes in the list evenly divides M.

3. Every number is evenly divisible by each prime in its prime decomposition.

These three facts lead to a contradiction. If M is not prime, then by the Fundamental Theorem of Arithmetic it must have a prime decomposition. Remember that the list supposedly contains all primes, so the numbers in the prime decomposition must be in this list somewhere. But none of these numbers evenly divides M! Therefore, none of them can be part of the prime decomposition of M.

This inconsistency, suggesting that M is not prime, yet has no prime decomposition, means that our original assertion of finitely many primes must be incorrect. The only alternative is that there are infinitely many primes.

Do not be discouraged if a first reading of the arguments above left you somewhat perplexed. The proof is abstract, and our brains are not naturally wired to think like this. It is not uncommon for students of mathematics to reread a proof many times before it starts to make sense.

Notice that the proof hinges on the truth of another theorem, the Fundamental Theorem of Arithmetic. We cheated a bit by simply accepting the truth of this theorem. In reality, the proof is usually carried out using other, weaker assumptions. However, the important takeaway is not the proof itself, but the *strategy* employed. Instead of trying to prove a claim directly, ask what happens if the opposite is assumed. If a recipe can be created to highlight an inconsistency, then there is no choice but to accept the original claim. We will see this strategy again in the future.

Even though there are infinitely many primes, their occurrence within the integers remains a mystery. In the 1960s the Polish mathematician Stanislaw Ulam unexpectedly uncovered a rather striking pattern. The graphical representation of his discovery is now known as an Ulam spiral in his honor. Its construction begins by writing all the integers in a square spiral, starting in the middle and rotating outward. Then all the prime numbers are shaded.

Starting in the middle with 1, the numbers spiral around with 2, 3, 4, and so on. The example below stops at 49, leaving a small 7 by 7 grid:

43	44	45	46	47	48	49
42	21	22	23	24	25	26
41	20	7	8	9	10	27
40	19	6	1	2	11	28
39	18	5	4	3	12	29
38	17	16	15	14	13	30
37	36	35	34	33	32	31

Start of an Ulam Spiral

At this scale, it is hard to discern any noteworthy patterns. As the grid grows we must zoom out in order to see the whole picture. To fit the image on the page we will also need to shrink the size of the squares, but that makes it difficult to read the numbers, so the labels will be left off. Squares representing prime numbers will be shaded black, and all others will be left blank. The picture on the next page shows the grid after it has been expanded to 200 by 200.

Note the strange diagonal lines that emerge. The grid can be made even larger, but the same diagonal patterns keep appearing. There are explanations for some of these patterns, but their existence remains largely a mystery. The placement of primes within the integers does not appear to be random, but their exact positioning is not fully understood.

Ultimately, primes have a special place in mathematics because they satisfy our human desire to break things down into their constituent parts. Think of the periodic table of elements, or small units of matter like atoms. It is surprising that the integers, our most basic abstract mathematical construct, are also assembled from the elemental quantities we call primes.

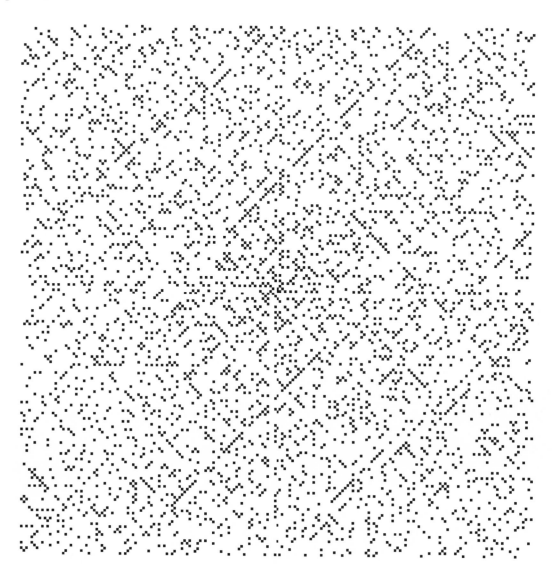

Example of 200x200 Ulam Spiral

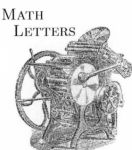

Infinite Sums & Geometric Series

Letter 11

Mathematics is the tool specially suited for dealing with abstract concepts of any kind and there is no limit to its power in this field.
-Paul Dirac

The concept of infinity does not arise often in our daily lives, and when it does, it is usually related to philosophical thought experiments. In mathematics, however, the concept of infinity is ubiquitous and of fundamental importance. In fact, we will devote an entire future letter to the concept of infinity. A particularly intriguing manifestation of this concept, known as an *infinite sum* (or *infinite series*), will be our focus here.

An infinite sum is exactly what it sounds like—a never-ending sum of numbers. Since it is not feasible to write down a sum with infinitely many terms, we will denote them by the first few terms followed by an ellipsis. The terms show the general pattern, and the ellipsis is meant to convey the infinite continuation of the pattern.

For example, the infinite sum shown below represents the sum of all the positive integers.

$$1 + 2 + 3 + 4 + ...$$

This is not a very interesting infinite sum; the result is clearly infinite. The infinite sums of interest have terms that get *smaller* as they progress.

Here is another example:

$$\frac{1}{1^2} + \frac{1}{2^2} + \frac{1}{3^2} + \frac{1}{4^2} + ...$$

This infinite sum adds all the reciprocals of square numbers (the reciprocal of a number n is simply $\frac{1}{n}$). Notice that as the sum advances, the denominator increases while the numerator stays the same; therefore each term is smaller than the one before it. These types of infinite sums are much more alluring since they may *converge* to something other than infinity. We will revisit this particular infinite sum in a future letter.

The two examples above should give a rough idea of how infinite sums are displayed. There are countless others, but we will focus on a special type of infinite sum known as a *geometric series*.

Before defining geometric series, a quick review of what it means to raise a number to a power will be helpful. Raising a number to a power is shorthand for multiplying the number by itself several times: $5^3 = 5 \cdot 5 \cdot 5 = 125$ and $4^5 = 4 \cdot 4 \cdot 4 \cdot 4 \cdot 4 = 1024$. Raising a fraction to a power works the same way: $\left(\frac{1}{2}\right)^3 = \left(\frac{1}{2}\right) \cdot \left(\frac{1}{2}\right) \cdot \left(\frac{1}{2}\right) = .5 \cdot .5 \cdot .5 = .125$.

One important special case is when a non-zero number is raised to the zeroth power. It turns out that *any* non-zero number raised to the zeroth power is equal to 1. This may seem a little strange, but this definition makes sense mathematically. For completeness, we'll give a brief explanation of why this is.

Envision 5 raised to the third power: $5^3 = 5 \cdot 5 \cdot 5$. Since multiplication by 1 does not change anything, this can also be written as: $5^3 = 1 \cdot 5 \cdot 5 \cdot 5$. If the power is 2, then $5^2 = 1 \cdot 5 \cdot 5$, and if the power is 1 then $5^1 = 1 \cdot 5$. Continuing this logic, if the power is 0 then there are no copies of 5, and all that is left is $5^0 = 1$. The same reasoning applies to any nonzero number raised to the power 0.

The first step in building a geometric series is to pick a fraction between 0 and 1. Let's start with $\frac{1}{2}$ as an example. The number is then raised to successively higher powers and summed—starting at 0 and increasing by 1 for each term. The first five terms of the geometric series for $\frac{1}{2}$ are:

$$\left(\frac{1}{2}\right)^0 + \left(\frac{1}{2}\right)^1 + \left(\frac{1}{2}\right)^2 + \left(\frac{1}{2}\right)^3 + \left(\frac{1}{2}\right)^4$$

To form the infinite sum this pattern would continue forever, but for the time being, we will restrict our attention to the first several terms.

The representation above is convenient because the pattern is visible, but using a calculator it can also be written in decimal format:

$$1 + .5 + .25 + .125 + .0625$$

Summing these 5 terms yields 1.9375.

A geometric series can be created for any fraction. For instance, here are the first four terms of the geometric series for the number $\frac{3}{4}$:

$$\left(\frac{3}{4}\right)^0 + \left(\frac{3}{4}\right)^1 + \left(\frac{3}{4}\right)^2 + \left(\frac{3}{4}\right)^3$$

Again, this can be written in decimal format instead:

$$1 + .75 + .5625 + .421875$$

The sum comes out to 2.734375.

Now we will do something that is quite common in mathematics—create an expression for a *generic* geometric series. Instead of choosing a specific number and a fixed number of terms, symbolic placeholders will be used. Here is the expression for the first n terms of a generic geometric series:

$$s = 1 + x + x^2 + x^3 + \ldots + x^{n-1} + x^n$$

The letter x is a placeholder for the fraction, like $\frac{1}{2}$ or $\frac{3}{4}$. The letter n is a placeholder for the highest power reached before ending. The terms x^{n-1} and x^n represent the last two terms in the series, and instead of writing x^0 for the first term, we have replaced it with a

1 (since $x^0 = 1$ for any choice of x). The ellipsis stands in for the remaining terms between x^3 and x^{n-1}. Finally, s is a placeholder for the actual result of the sum. As a concrete example, letting $x = \frac{1}{2}$ and $n = 4$ gives the five term geometric series from above that sums to $s = 1.9375$.

Why is this symbolic expression useful? Well, it allows us to prove results for *all* geometric series without choosing specific numbers. Our goal will be to find a succinct expression for s, the sum of the series.

To accomplish this, a sequence of specific operations will be performed. Walking through this derivation reveals how mathematicians are able to extract beautiful results from messy expressions. In what follows, always keep in mind that the symbols are just placeholders for numbers.

We will begin by multiplying both sides of the expression by x. Remember that multiplying both sides of an equation by the same number does not affect the equality:

$$x \cdot s = x \cdot (1 + x + x^2 + x^3 + ... + x^{n-1} + x^n)$$

Next, we will employ the *distributive* property of multiplication. As a reminder, here is a concrete example that distributes a 2 across the sum $1 + 3 + 5$:

$$2 \cdot (1 + 3 + 5) = 2 \cdot 1 + 2 \cdot 3 + 2 \cdot 5$$

The left and right sides of this equality represent two ways of writing the same thing.

Our equation involving x will look a bit more complicated, but the idea is the same as the concrete example above. Distributing the x on the right side yields:

$$x \cdot s = x \cdot 1 + x \cdot x + x \cdot x^2 + x \cdot x^3 + ... + x \cdot x^{n-1} + x \cdot x^n$$

Observe how each term on the right is now multiplied by a copy of x.

Let's consider each term in this sum. The first term $x \cdot 1$ is easy—it is just equal to x. The next term is another way of writing x^2, so x^2 can be written in place of $x \cdot x$. Likewise, $x \cdot x^2$ is the same as x^3, $x \cdot x^3$ is the same as x^4, and so on. Multiplying by x simply raises the power on each term by 1. Therefore, an equivalent way to write this sum is:

$$x \cdot s = x + x^2 + x^3 + x^4 + ... + x^n + x^{n+1}$$

Importantly, the last two terms each have their powers increased by 1; the power $n - 1$ becomes $(n - 1) + 1 = n$ and the highest power n becomes $n + 1$.

The second step is to add 1 to both sides of the equation. This gives:

$$1 + x \cdot s = 1 + x + x^2 + x^3 + x^4 + ... + x^n + x^{n+1}$$

Now for the most important step. If you cover up the very last term x^{n+1} on the right, the remaining expression $1 + x + x^2 + x^3 + x^4 + ... + x^n$ should look familiar (it isn't written explicitly but the term x^{n-1} appears directly before x^n). This is the original sum s that we started with! So we can substitute s in place of $1 + x + x^2 + x^3 + x^4 + ... + x^n$. The resulting expression is:

$$1 + x \cdot s = s + x^{n+1}$$

This is great progress. Through a series of manipulations, we have collapsed the equation down to only a few terms. The last steps are relatively easy. Since our goal is to arrive at a nice formula for s, we need to isolate s on one side.

Subtract x^{n+1} from both sides to get:

$$1 + x \cdot s - x^{n+1} = s$$

The term x^{n+1} disappears from the right side because $x^{n+1} - x^{n+1} = 0$.

Similarly, subtract $x \cdot s$ from both sides:

$$1 - x^{n+1} = s - x \cdot s$$

Let's also pull out the common factor of s on the right side. The subtraction $s - x \cdot s$ is equivalent to $(1 - x) \cdot s$. In other words $s - x \cdot s = (1 - x) \cdot s$. If this expression is read from right to left it is nothing more than the distributive property of multiplication discussed earlier.

Pulling out the common factor of s gives:

$$1 - x^{n+1} = (1 - x) \cdot s$$

The very last step is to divide both sides by $1 - x$. This will cancel the $(1 - x)$ term on the right side since $\frac{1-x}{1-x} = 1$. Only s remains on the right side:

$$\frac{1 - x^{n+1}}{1 - x} = s$$

This is quite an amazing result—the geometric series has been reduced into a relatively simple expression. Quite a few steps were required to get here, but each step obeyed the rules of algebra and arithmetic. Verifying each step takes some patience—it is not too dissimilar from learning a new language (albeit a rather abstract one).

This formula can be verified using the two examples from earlier. The first example was five terms long using the fraction $\frac{1}{2}$, and the final sum s was 1.9375. Using the formula, substitute $\frac{1}{2}$ for x and replace n with the highest power in the series, which was 4:

$$\frac{1 - \left(\frac{1}{2}\right)^{4+1}}{1 - \left(\frac{1}{2}\right)}$$

Let's write this in decimal format by replacing $\frac{1}{2}$ with .5 and 5 in place of $4 + 1$.

$$\frac{1 - .5^5}{1 - .5}$$

Using a calculator this comes out to the correct answer:

$$\frac{1 - .5^5}{1 - .5} = 1.9375$$

The second example used $\frac{3}{4}$ and continued to the power 3, so x will be $\frac{3}{4}$ and n will be 3. Plugging these numbers into the formula gives:

$$\frac{1 - \left(\frac{3}{4}\right)^{3+1}}{1 - \left(\frac{3}{4}\right)} = 2.734375$$

Again we arrive at the correct answer.

While this formula is useful for geometric series with a finite number of terms, what happens for an *infinite* geometric series? Does the final sum keep growing beyond all bounds? After all, the sum would contain infinitely many non-zero numbers. On the other hand, the terms of the series become incredibly small as the powers rise, so maybe the numbers shrink fast enough to prevent the final sum from growing to infinity.

What happens to the formula for s as n goes to infinity? Remember, the formula:

$$\frac{1 - x^{n+1}}{1 - x}$$

is *exactly* the same as:

$$1 + x + x^2 + x^3 + ... + x^{n-1} + x^n$$

So letting n go to infinity is equivalent to extending the geometric series to infinitely many terms.

Note that in the formula, n is only present in the x^{n+1} term. Therefore, the question of what happens when a geometric series is extended indefinitely can be answered by studying what happens to x^{n+1} as n goes to infinity.

There is a good reason we chose to focus on geometric series for fractions between 0 and 1— any number in this interval decreases and eventually *converges* to 0 as it is raised to higher and higher powers. The topic of convergence is intimately tied to the concept of infinity, and we will spend more time on convergence in a future letter. For our purposes here, the main point is that x^{n+1} becomes 0 as n grows to infinity—as long as the number x is strictly between 0 and 1.

As an example, look what happens as the number $\frac{1}{2}$ is raised to higher and higher powers (rounding to 10 decimal places):

$$\left(\frac{1}{2}\right)^{15} = .0000305176 \qquad \left(\frac{1}{2}\right)^{20} = .0000009537 \qquad \left(\frac{1}{2}\right)^{25} = .0000000298$$

At power 25 the result is already a very small number. In fact, if the last number was rounded to only 5 decimal places, it *would* be 0. Imagine raising $\frac{1}{2}$ to the power 100, 1000, or 10000; the powers above are still relatively puny compared to letting n grow into the millions, billions, and beyond toward infinity.

The final result shown below reveals the true beauty of infinite geometric series. As n goes to infinity, the term x^{n+1} in the expression:

$$\frac{1 - x^{n+1}}{1 - x} = s$$

converges to 0, and the formula becomes:

$$\frac{1}{1 - x} = s$$

What does this mean exactly? Using $x = \frac{1}{2}$, it means that the infinite geometric series:

$$\left(\frac{1}{2}\right)^0 + \left(\frac{1}{2}\right)^1 + \left(\frac{1}{2}\right)^2 + \left(\frac{1}{2}\right)^3 + \left(\frac{1}{2}\right)^4 + \left(\frac{1}{2}\right)^5 + \left(\frac{1}{2}\right)^6 + \dots$$

is equal to:

$$\frac{1}{1 - \left(\frac{1}{2}\right)} = 2$$

Here is the full expression for completeness:

$$\left(\frac{1}{2}\right)^0 + \left(\frac{1}{2}\right)^1 + \left(\frac{1}{2}\right)^2 + \left(\frac{1}{2}\right)^3 + \left(\frac{1}{2}\right)^4 + \left(\frac{1}{2}\right)^5 + \left(\frac{1}{2}\right)^6 + \dots = 2$$

As usual, the three dots at the end imply that the terms go on forever. Even though the sum contains infinitely many terms, the rising powers force them toward 0 fast enough for the sum to converge. Furthermore, it converges to a nice whole number!

It is helpful to *visualize* the summation above. Imagine a line segment exactly 1 unit long:

Now place two of these line segments side by side for a total length of 2 (the label of the second one will be left off):

Let's cut the second line segment in half and label the length of the first half, but leave the remaining half blank:

Next, the remaining half will be cut in half again to give two pieces of length $\frac{1}{4}$. As before, we'll label the leftmost one:

One more iteration of cutting the remaining $\frac{1}{4}$ piece in half produces two $\frac{1}{8}$ pieces. Labeling the leftmost one gives:

The numbers above can be rewritten in terms of powers of $\frac{1}{2}$. Note that each time the line segment is cut in half, the length is multiplied by $\frac{1}{2}$. On the third cut, the length is:

$$\frac{1}{8} = \left(\frac{1}{2}\right) \cdot \left(\frac{1}{2}\right) \cdot \left(\frac{1}{2}\right) = \left(\frac{1}{2}\right)^3$$

The first line segment can be written using the power 0 since $\left(\frac{1}{2}\right)^0 = 1$.

These are the first four terms of the geometric series for $\frac{1}{2}$. This process can continue indefinitely, dividing the remaining piece into ever smaller equal halves, and each split adds one more term to the geometric series for $\frac{1}{2}$.

From the picture, it is clear that the sum of all the small pieces will approach 2—the total length of the line segment. This is the intuition behind the infinite geometric series for $\frac{1}{2}$.

The elegance of the final formula stems from the fact that it works for *any* number between 0 and 1. What is the infinite geometric series for $\frac{3}{4}$? The formula can be used to see that it is equal to 4.

How about a different number, like $\frac{1}{3}$? The formula yields:

$$\left(\frac{1}{3}\right)^0 + \left(\frac{1}{3}\right)^1 + \left(\frac{1}{3}\right)^2 + \left(\frac{1}{3}\right)^3 + \left(\frac{1}{3}\right)^4 + \left(\frac{1}{3}\right)^5 + \left(\frac{1}{3}\right)^6 + \ldots = 1.5$$

Infinite geometric series are rather unique because they converge to a finite number *and* there is a formula to compute that number. In general, not all infinite series converge; moreover, it is not always a trivial task to work out the final answer when they do.

There is one last extraordinary infinite series we will mention. In a previous letter, we encountered the concept of continuous growth and the special irrational number $e = 2.71828....$ This result was discovered by letting n go to infinity in the following expression:

$$\left(1 + \frac{1}{n}\right)^n$$

Surprisingly, it turns out that e can also be represented as an infinite series.

We need to introduce one additional concept before writing the infinite series for e—the *factorial*. The factorial of an integer n is written as:

$$n!$$

and consists of the product of all integers up to and including n.

For instance, here are the factorials of the first 5 positive integers:

$$1! = 1$$
$$2! = 2 \cdot 1$$
$$3! = 3 \cdot 2 \cdot 1$$
$$4! = 4 \cdot 3 \cdot 2 \cdot 1$$
$$5! = 5 \cdot 4 \cdot 3 \cdot 2 \cdot 1$$

So $3! = 6$, $4! = 24$, and $5! = 120$; the factorials grow quite rapidly.

There is one special case. The factorial of 0 is defined to be $0! = 1$. The reasoning behind this is similar to raising a number to the zeroth power. We can multiply the factorials by an extra factor of 1 without changing anything:

$$1! = 1 \cdot 1$$
$$2! = 2 \cdot 1 \cdot 1$$
$$3! = 3 \cdot 2 \cdot 1 \cdot 1$$

Reading from right to left, there is a default factor of 1 followed by a count up to the final number. With $0!$ we start with the default factor of 1, but that is where it ends—there is no need to count up to anything. So $0!$ is defined to be 1.

How do factorials relate to e? It is rather astounding, but e is exactly equal to the infinite sum of the factorial reciprocals:

$$\frac{1}{0!} + \frac{1}{1!} + \frac{1}{2!} + \frac{1}{3!} + \frac{1}{4!} + \frac{1}{5!} + \ldots = e$$

Notice that $0! = 1$ and $1! = 1$, so the first 2 terms are both equal to 1. The sum can be validated by adding up the first several terms using a calculator; it quickly approaches the true value of $e = 2.71828\ldots$.

If you are skeptical of the findings we've covered above, you are not alone. Most new mathematics students react with a mix of awe and disbelief when they first encounter infinite series. The fact that adding together infinitely many non-zero quantities can result in a finite number defies intuition, and claiming that the sum of an infinite series is *exactly* equal to a particular number is equally mind-boggling. A future letter on infinity and convergence will deepen our understanding of these results.

Pascal's Triangle

Letter 12

Mathematics compares the most diverse phenomena and discovers the secret analogies that unite them.
-Joseph Fourier

In previous letters we encountered situations where the repeated application of simple rules gave rise to complex behavior: Conway's Game of Life, fractals, and feedback loops to name a few. The object of study today, known as *Pascal's triangle*, shares a common trait with these examples—it is constructed using simple rules. In fact, the only required operation is addition. The name of the French mathematician Blaise Pascal has been attached to the triangle since the early 18th century, although it was known prior to his era. Pascal published a comprehensive treatise compiling its many useful patterns, some of which we will explore below.

First, we need to construct the triangle. In essence, it is nothing more than a grid of numbers, and the triangle shape arises naturally. It is easiest to start with a grid of zeros containing a single 1 in the middle of the top row:

0	0	0	0	1	0	0	0	0
0	0	0	0	0	0	0	0	0
0	0	0	0	0	0	0	0	0
0	0	0	0	0	0	0	0	0

Filling in the base of the triangle is accomplished by following a single rule: the number in the next row is the sum of the numbers above to the right and above to the left.

Let's write out the next 3 rows and review:

0	0	0	0	1	0	0	0	0
0	0	0	1	0	1	0	0	0
0	0	1	0	2	0	1	0	0
0	1	0	3	0	3	0	1	0

Consider the very last row and notice that each number is the sum of the two numbers above it to the left and right. The same pattern holds for every number except the very first row containing a single 1. The 1s along the outer edge are the sum of the numbers 1 and 0.

If the 0s are removed the triangle shape emerges:

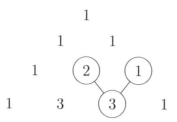

This is how the triangle is usually presented, and it is easy to see how the numbers in each row combine to create the next. As one last visual reminder, a 3 in the bottom row is circled along with the 2 and 1 that add to it.

Now that the construction is apparent, let's fill in several more rows:

$$
\begin{array}{ccccccccccccccccccccc}
 & & & & & & & & & & 1 & & & & & & & & & & \\
 & & & & & & & & & 1 & & 1 & & & & & & & & & \\
 & & & & & & & & 1 & & 2 & & 1 & & & & & & & & \\
 & & & & & & & 1 & & 3 & & 3 & & 1 & & & & & & & \\
 & & & & & & 1 & & 4 & & 6 & & 4 & & 1 & & & & & & \\
 & & & & & 1 & & 5 & & 10 & & 10 & & 5 & & 1 & & & & & \\
 & & & & 1 & & 6 & & 15 & & 20 & & 15 & & 6 & & 1 & & & & \\
 & & & 1 & & 7 & & 21 & & 35 & & 35 & & 21 & & 7 & & 1 & & & \\
 & & 1 & & 8 & & 28 & & 56 & & 70 & & 56 & & 28 & & 8 & & 1 & & \\
 & 1 & & 9 & & 36 & & 84 & & 126 & & 126 & & 84 & & 36 & & 9 & & 1 & \\
1 & & 10 & & 45 & & 120 & & 210 & & 252 & & 210 & & 120 & & 45 & & 10 & & 1 \\
\end{array}
$$

$$1 \quad 11 \quad 55 \quad 165 \quad 330 \quad 462 \quad 462 \quad 330 \quad 165 \quad 55 \quad 11 \quad 1$$

The rows can be computed forever, but this will suffice for our purposes. Take a moment to select a few numbers and verify that each is the sum of the two numbers above it.

Our exploration of the many patterns concealed within the triangle begins with the rows. What happens if a single row is summed? Here are the sums of the first 6 rows:

$$1 = 1$$
$$1 + 1 = 2$$
$$1 + 2 + 1 = 4$$
$$1 + 3 + 3 + 1 = 8$$
$$1 + 4 + 6 + 4 + 1 = 16$$
$$1 + 5 + 10 + 10 + 5 + 1 = 32$$

If the rows are numbered starting with 0, then the sum of row n is exactly 2^n. For instance, the last row summed above is considered row 5 (since the top row is counted as row 0), and the sum of its entries gives $32 = 2^5$. The sum of the row before it, row 4, is $16 = 2^4$, and so on. Recall that any positive number to the power 0 is 1, so row 0 fits the pattern too with $1 = 2^0$.

This is rather surprising considering the fact that only addition has been used up to this point—there is no reason to expect powers of 2 to appear. Nonetheless, every row happens to give a symmetric sum that adds to a power of 2.

Here is another peculiar pattern. Choose any 1 on the outer edge of the triangle as a starting point. Now move down a diagonal path into the triangle, summing the numbers along the way. At any point, change direction to the opposite downward diagonal, creating an "L" pattern. The final number on the opposite diagonal below the direction change will always be the sum of the numbers followed to get there.

Three examples of this appear below. The paths start on the outer edge and follow the circled numbers on the chosen diagonal. At a random stopping point the direction switches to create an "L" pattern, and the very last number shaded in gray is the sum of the circled numbers on the path preceding it.

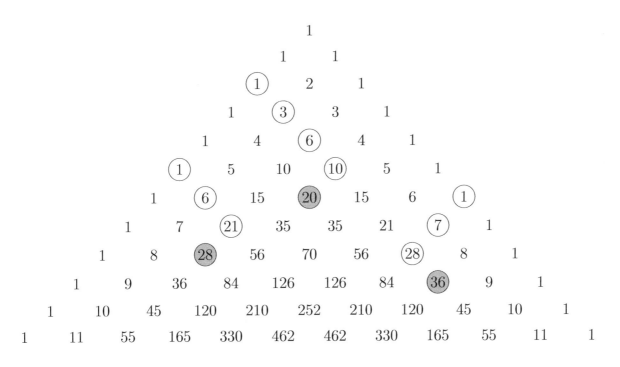

This pattern holds true regardless of the starting point on the outer edge, and regardless of where the direction changes. The ending number will always be the sum of the preceding diagonal. This strange relationship between the diagonals is certainly not expected from the outset.

Remarkably, the prime numbers play a role in the triangle as well. The outer edges consist of all 1s, and the first inner diagonals contain the integers $1, 2, 3, 4, \ldots$. Let's move down these two inner diagonals and circle all the prime numbers.

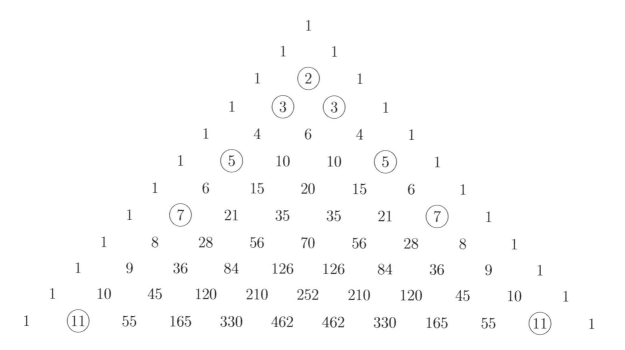

The first surprise is that the prime numbers *only* show up on these first inner diagonals. Only the first several rows of the triangle are displayed, but in reality it has infinitely many rows, and therefore the interior contains infinitely many integers. Intuitively, it seems like a prime number would be produced in the interior at *some* point. However, it turns out that not a single prime number is ever produced in the interior of the triangle beyond the first inner diagonals.

There is one other interesting feature concerning the arrangement of primes. Examine the numbers in the rows with a circled prime on either side; the numbers 10 and 10 occur between the two circled 5s and the numbers 21, 35, 35, and 21 occur between the two circled 7s. If a row contains a prime, then *all* the numbers in the interior of that row are divisible by that prime—10 is divisible by 5, and both 21 and 35 are divisible by 7. Let's verify this for the row containing 11 as well. The numbers 55, 165, 330, and 462 are all multiples of 11, and so divisible by 11:

$$55 = 5 \cdot 11$$
$$165 = 15 \cdot 11$$
$$330 = 30 \cdot 11$$
$$462 = 42 \cdot 11$$

This strange property holds for the entire infinite triangle. At no point during the construction is any consideration given to prime numbers or divisibility, yet this pattern spontaneously emerges.

There is also a famous number sequence hidden within the triangle. It shows up within the "shallow diagonals", the first eight of which are outlined next.

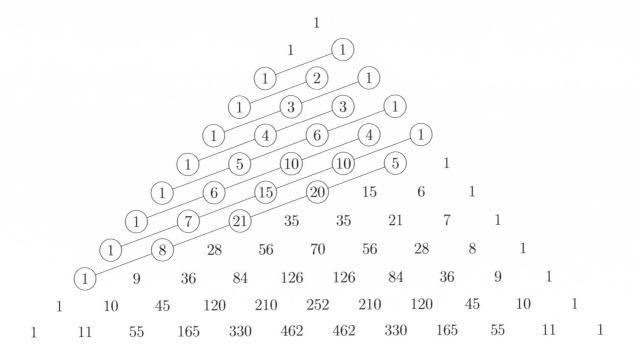

Look what happens if the numbers in each diagonal are summed:

$$1 + 1 = 2$$
$$1 + 2 = 3$$
$$1 + 3 + 1 = 5$$
$$1 + 4 + 3 = 8$$
$$1 + 5 + 6 + 1 = 13$$
$$1 + 6 + 10 + 4 = 21$$
$$1 + 7 + 15 + 10 + 1 = 34$$
$$1 + 8 + 21 + 20 + 5 = 55$$

Does the sequence $2, 3, 5, 8, 13, 21, 34, 55$ look familiar? This is the start of the famous Fibonacci sequence! It is typically constructed recursively, summing the previous 2 terms to generate the next. However, the shallow diagonals on the triangle provide an alternative way to generate the entire sequence.

There is a particularly useful pattern that the triangle is well known for, and it stems from a famous problem in combinatorics. If there are n different objects, how many groupings of k objects can be formed? As an example, suppose there are 5 people whom we'll label A, B, C, D, and E. How many different teams of size 3 can be formed? In this example $n = 5$ (the people) and $k = 3$ (the team size). Using trial and error, here are all the possible combinations:

A, B, C   A, D, E   B, D, E   A, C, E   C, E, B

A, C, D   B, C, D   C, D, E   B, D, A   A, B, E

There are 10 possible teams. Notice that the ordering does not matter; the group A, B, C is considered the same as B, C, A or C, A, B.

How about teams of 4 people? Without too much effort we can write down all possibilities. They are:

A, B, C, D   B, C, D, E   A, B, C, E   A, C, D, E   A, B, D, E

So there are 5 possible teams of 4 people.

This exercise is sometimes referred to as the "n choose k" problem. Given n distinct objects, the goal is to determine *how many* different groups of size k can be formed.

What if the group size is increased to 10 people, then how many teams of size 4 can be formed? In this case $n = 10$ and $k = 4$. Can this be computed by listing all combinations as before? It is possible, but as n grows, it becomes significantly more difficult.

Luckily, the answer to the n choose k problem can be read directly from Pascal's triangle. In fact, it can be read directly from the nth row and kth column. The first example with $n = 5$ and $k = 3$ resulted in 10 different teams. To find this answer, count down 5 rows along the left edge and move 3 columns to the right. The only caveat is that you must start the row and column counts from 0; the very top row is considered row 0, and the leftmost column is considered column 0. The answer is circled in the 5th row and 3rd column below:

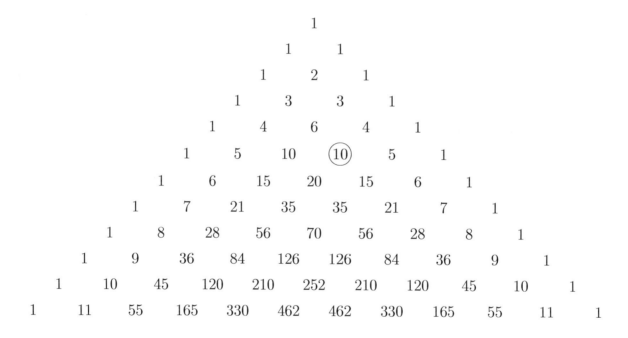

Moving one more number to the right gives the answer to the $n = 5$ choose $k = 4$ problem, which is 5. Likewise, counting down 10 rows and over 4 columns gives the answer to the proposed $n = 10$ choose $k = 4$ problem, which is 210. When moving down the rows and across the columns remember to start counting from 0.

The answer to the $n = 100$ choose $k = 7$ problem could be read off of the 100th row and 7th column. Of course, it would be monotonous to compute so many rows of the triangle, but it only requires simple addition. In contrast, *directly* computing the n choose k problem through trial and error becomes relatively complex for n much larger than 10. It is quite surprising that the answer to this problem materializes so cleanly in the triangle.

There is one last mysterious property we will highlight—a famous fractal is hidden within Pascal's triangle. To uncover it, let's first bring the numbers closer together and draw a box around each. Next, we will shade in all the *odd* numbers.

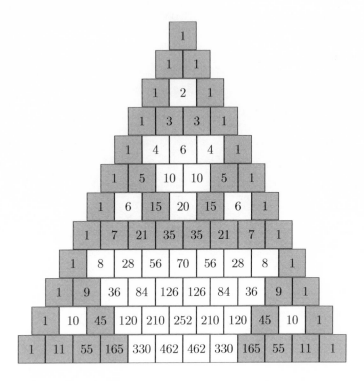

This may not look like much yet, but it will start to come into focus as the size is increased. The second picture is produced by computing more rows and, once again, only shading the odd numbers.

As the size of the triangle increases, we encounter a problem. The numbers become very large, and fitting them onto the page is not feasible. Therefore, we will increase the size of the triangle one more time, but the numbers will not be printed. The shading rule for the final picture remains the same, but black shading will be used for a crisper look.

This is the famous Sierpiński fractal encountered in an earlier letter! Recall that our original construction of the Sierpiński triangle used a handful of rules for shrinking and stacking triangles. It is astonishing that this fractal also happens to be embedded within Pascal's triangle; there is no obvious reason to think that the simple rules used to construct the triangle would in any way relate to the Sierpiński fractal. It is a truly unexpected connection.

The results highlighted in this letter are by no means exhaustive. In fact, we'll revisit a feature of the triangle related to probabilities in a future letter. It is amazing how many patterns such a simple object can hold.

Infinity & Limits

Letter 13

In mathematics, you don't understand things. You just get used to them.
-John von Neumann

Although it is heavily used throughout mathematics, the concept of infinity is difficult to grasp. Humans tend to learn through examples and analogies, but there are few analogies, and even fewer (if any) real-world examples of the infinite.

When contemplating the infinite we tend to gravitate toward the very large, like the vastness of the universe. However, instead of grappling with the very large, an alternative idea is to consider the very small. For instance, imagine a 12 inch ruler. Now cut it in half to obtain a 6 inch ruler, and then again to create a 3 inch ruler. Can this process continue *forever*? Practically speaking, no. Even with precise tools, the atomic level will eventually come into focus and atoms will need to be examined. Despite current technology, is it at least theoretically possible to keep splitting the ruler forever? Particles of matter smaller than atoms are known to exist, but what lies beyond that level is anyone's guess. In the end, the infinite divisibility of matter seems to be as unknowable as the size of the universe.

Here is another example to ponder—is there a smallest unit of time? In other words, can one second be split in half forever? This is a strange concept to consider, and like the infinite divisibility of matter, it is impossible to give a decisive answer.

These brief thought experiments illustrate the difficulty of comprehending infinity by way of example. Fortunately, the concept of infinity as it is used in mathematics is slightly easier to understand.

To begin, it is important to realize that infinity *is not a number*, it is a *concept*. To remind yourself of this, think of what happens if you add 1 to infinity. The result is the same— infinity. There are no such numbers where this is true. In fact, the concept of adding 1 to infinity is meaningless in the first place; it is not a number, so trying to perform calculations with it is silly. That being said, there *is* a way to assign a magnitude to infinity—but we will save that topic for a future letter.

We'll leverage a common mathematical framework to help guide our study of infinity. The trick is to frame the idea as a two-player game—a game that we can always win. Eventually, this framework will be used to explain the most important application of infinity, the concept of a *limit*. Before delving into limits, let's outline a simple example of the two-player game idea. It is comparable to a proof by contradiction.

Consider the positive integers $1, 2, 3, 4, \ldots$. Can we claim that there are infinitely many integers? Of course we can, but how to prove it? One approach is to devise a method that refutes any argument to the contrary, and this is where the idea of the two-player game is helpful.

Envision yourself as the first player, and the other as someone who claims that there are *not* infinitely many integers. If the other player is right then the integers must stop somewhere, and the last number is, by definition, the largest overall integer. Ask the other player to write this integer down. Let's use the symbol b (for *b*ig) to denote it. You win the game by showing that there is an integer larger than b. Well, consider the number $b + 1$. This is still an integer, and it is certainly larger than b, so you win. The crucial point is that you can *always* win this game—no matter what integer b the other player writes down, forming the integer $b + 1$ shows that a still larger integer exists.

Admittedly, this is a strange way to frame the problem. First of all, adding 1 to the number the other player writes down seems arbitrary (in fact adding 2, 3, 4 or any other positive integer would achieve the same goal). The process also seems somewhat trivial. If the other player claims that the largest number is one trillion, then adding 1 to this number and countering that one trillion one is larger just seems too simplistic. Nonetheless, the argument works, and a process that disproves every example implies that the other player's original assertion must be false. The only alternative is to accept that there are indeed infinitely many integers. This is the key to understanding the use of infinity within mathematics.

A similar technique can be used to prove the infinite divisibility of our familiar number system. Is there a smallest unit that cannot be divided any further? The number .001 is small, but the number .0001 is smaller, and .00001 is smaller still; is there a stopping point?

Dividing a number into smaller and smaller pieces can certainly continue forever. Once again, we can prove this claim by framing it as a game. Suppose someone says that yes, there *is* a smallest positive number. Ask them to write it down—let's use the symbol s (for *s*mall) to denote this number. Now multiply s by .5 to obtain the new number $.5 \cdot s$. This number is half the size of s and therefore smaller, so we win.

Multiplying instead of subtracting from s is a simple way to guarantee that the resulting number is smaller but still positive. Once again, we can demonstrate the claim by constructing an actual number to disprove the other player.

The "proofs" above are not especially groundbreaking. It is almost self-evident that yes, there are infinitely many integers; dividing a number down into smaller pieces forever is not particularly shocking either. The main reason for these examples is to illustrate a new way of thinking. Instead of trying to prove the claim directly, this indirect approach allows us to discredit any argument to the contrary.

We are now in a position to discuss *limits*, the most important idea connected to the concept of infinity within mathematics. We have encountered limits a few times in earlier letters; most notably in the letter on infinite sums and geometric series. The trick to understanding limits lies in applying the two-player game analogy.

To introduce limits, consider the fraction below. The symbol n is a placeholder for any

positive integer:
$$\frac{1}{n}$$

What happens to this fraction as n grows to infinity? It is important to realize that we cannot simply plug infinity in for n, since infinity is not a number. Instead, envision n growing toward infinity starting at 1 and increasing by 1 each second. This would generate the sequence:
$$\frac{1}{1}, \frac{1}{2}, \frac{1}{3}, \frac{1}{4}, \frac{1}{5}, \frac{1}{6}, \dots$$

The goal is to uncover what happens to this sequence as n grows without bound, and the term *limit* is used to convey this idea: what is the limit of $\frac{1}{n}$ as n goes to infinity? The limit is so important in mathematics that it even has its own notation. In symbols, the question is:
$$\lim_{n \to \infty} \frac{1}{n} = ?$$

The limit asks for a single number to replace the question mark. The term *converge* is also often used to express this idea, and can be worded as: what does $\frac{1}{n}$ converge to as n goes to infinity?

There are two points worth mentioning before proceeding. First of all, not all expressions will have a limit. As an example, the expression n^2 does not have a limit as n goes to infinity; it simply grows without bound and does not converge to any finite number.

The second point, and this is the primary puzzle when dealing with limits, is that it is up to us to propose a number for the limit. We claim that the limit of $\frac{1}{n}$ as n goes to infinity is 0:
$$\lim_{n \to \infty} \frac{1}{n} = 0$$

This happens to be a fairly intuitive guess since the number $\frac{1}{n}$ certainly gets smaller as n increases. Unfortunately, it is not always obvious what the limit might be, or whether one even exists. For example, recall the expression:
$$\left(1 + \frac{1}{n}\right)^n$$

from a previous letter on continuous growth. Deciphering the limit in this case is much more challenging—indeed it is not even clear that one exists (it turned out to be the special number e).

We have proposed a limit of 0 for the expression $\frac{1}{n}$ as n goes to infinity. What is really meant by this is that as n goes to infinity, the expression $\frac{1}{n}$ becomes *indistinguishable* from 0. What does it mean for a number to be indistinguishable from another? Well, it comes down to precision.

Is the number .1 indistinguishable from 0? No, of course not. How about the number .000001? The difference is tiny, but at least on a computer, these would be considered two different numbers. How about .00000000001? If a calculator only had 10 decimal places of precision, the difference between this number and 0 would be indistinguishable—at least to the calculator.

In the precise world of mathematics, though, there is still a difference between the numbers .00000000001 and 0. This leads to an obvious question: is there a precision level beyond which errors do not matter? This occurs frequently in real life, for instance when measuring boards to within $\frac{1}{16}$ of an inch for a bookshelf.

Unfortunately, we cannot simply choose a finite precision level in mathematics—there would be widespread disagreement as to which level is acceptable. However, what if we could please everyone by proving that their precision level could always be reached?

Let's illustrate this idea using the example expression $\frac{1}{n}$ and the two-player game framework from earlier. Suppose someone disagrees and claims that $\frac{1}{n}$ does not become 0 as n goes to infinity. The immediate question is then: if the limit is not 0, then how far from 0 is it? This will force a precision level. Say the other person claims that no matter how large n becomes, it will always be at least .00001 away from 0. Now how to prove them wrong and win the game? Notice that .00001 written as a fraction is $\frac{1}{100000}$. If the denominator is increased by 1 to 100001, then the number $\frac{1}{100001}$ is smaller than the precision level of .00001:

$$\frac{1}{100001} = .00000999990... < .00001$$

Therefore, if n is chosen to be strictly larger than 100000, then the expression $\frac{1}{n}$ will be *closer* to zero than their precision level, and we will win the game. In other words, truncating at only 5 decimal places of precision, the number $\frac{1}{n}$ would be indistinguishable from 0 as n grows beyond 100001.

No matter which precision level is suggested, let's call it p, we can always go beyond it by choosing n to be any number larger than $\frac{1}{p}$. In the scenario above the precision level was $p = .00001$, and it can be satisfied by choosing any n larger than $\frac{1}{.00001} = 100000$. If someone argues a smaller precision level, say that the limit is .000001 away from 0, then set $p = .000001$ and win the game by considering any n larger than $\frac{1}{.000001} = 1000000$.

The point is that this method is able to satisfy any precision level. The limit signifies what happens to $\frac{1}{n}$ as n grows beyond all bounds, and we can always move beyond a given precision level by making n as large as we need. If the limit of $\frac{1}{n}$ is not different from 0 at *any* precision level, then it must be exactly 0.

Let's look at a few other limits encountered in previous letters. The letter on geometric series ended with this astounding result:

$$\left(\frac{1}{2}\right)^0 + \left(\frac{1}{2}\right)^1 + \left(\frac{1}{2}\right)^2 + \left(\frac{1}{2}\right)^3 + \left(\frac{1}{2}\right)^4 + \left(\frac{1}{2}\right)^5 + \left(\frac{1}{2}\right)^6 + ... = 2$$

This is an infinite sum of numbers, and as before, the ellipsis at the end is shorthand for "continue on like this forever". Notice that the resulting sum is exactly equal to 2. This is really a limit in disguise! What this expression actually claims is that the *limit* of this sum is 2. Specifically, as the number of terms goes to infinity, this sum converges to the limit of 2.

To prove that this infinite sum is exactly equal to 2 we can force a precision level and figure out how many terms must be computed to beat it. There are infinitely many terms in the sum, so we can always compute more of them. As more terms are computed, the sum will get closer and closer to 2, eventually beating any precision level.

Another limit appeared in our letter on the golden rectangle and Fibonacci sequence. One striking result was that the ratio of successive Fibonacci numbers converged to the golden ratio of 1.618.... To prove that this is the correct limit we would take the same approach. Any claim that the limit is not exactly equal to the golden ratio can be countered by asking for a precision level. If it is not equal to the golden ratio, then how far away is it? Given any precision level, we can always beat it by computing terms further and further out in the Fibonacci sequence.

The idea of a limit extends beyond numerical calculations. For example, fractals can be viewed as a type of "geometric" limit. When we formed the Sierpiński triangle in an earlier letter, a set of rules was applied to an equilateral triangle over and over (shrink, copy, stack). The "limit" of these operations turned out to be a fractal. Unlike numerical limits which are easy to write down, geometric limits like fractals can only be rendered as approximations on a screen.

An earlier letter on randomness and Buffon's Needle also contained a limit. As a reminder, the setup for Buffon's Needle problem was a wooden plank floor along with a sewing needle as long as the planks are wide. For each random toss of the needle we recorded whether it crossed two floor boards or not. Finally, the quantity shown below was computed:

$$2 \cdot \left(\frac{\# \text{ Tosses}}{\# \text{ Times Crosses Planks}} \right)$$

The remarkable outcome was that this number approached π as the tosses progressed. Phrased using our new terminology, the *limit* of this expression is π as the number of tosses goes to infinity.

Here is one final example. Is the following equality true?

$$.999... = 1$$

The three trailing dots imply the infinite continuation of 9s after the decimal point. This simple claim is liable to spark a lively debate if you are unfamiliar with limits.

For a better understanding of what this statement asserts, imagine the following sequence of numbers:

$$x_1 = .9 \quad x_2 = .99 \quad x_3 = .999 \quad x_4 = .9999 \quad ... \quad x_n = .999...9$$

Each term x_n has precisely n 9s after the decimal point.

Now that we know about limits, we can ask what happens as n goes to infinity. It turns out that the limit is equal to 1:

$$\lim_{n \to \infty} x_n = 1$$

To convince yourself of this, think back to the two player game analogy. If the limit is not 1, then how far away from 1 is it? Suppose someone claims that the numbers x_n will always be at least .0001 away from 1. To prove them wrong, all you need to do is go out into the sequence and select a term that beats this precision level. The 5th term $x_5 = .99999$ will do since $1 - x_5 = .00001 < .0001$. It isn't too difficult to see that this can be done for *any* precision level, because there are infinitey many x_n to choose from. Therefore, the limit must be exactly 1.

The statement .999... = 1 is actually an informal way of expressing this limit:

$$.999... = \lim_{n \to \infty} x_n = 1$$

Although none of the x_n are exactly equal to 1, the limit of x_n as n goes to infinity, informally represented as .999..., is indeed equal to 1.

These examples should help illuminate a few murky results from earlier letters. Limits and the concept of infinity underpin much of modern mathematics, and understanding limits requires a new way of thinking. It is interesting to note that the entire foundation of calculus (the subject of a future letter) is built upon the concept of limits, and the tools of calculus are especially useful for modeling real-world problems. This is in spite of the fact that the concept of infinity, something which may not even exist in the real world, plays such a vital role.

Goldbach's Conjecture
Letter 14

Some mathematician, I believe, has said that true pleasure lies not in the discovery of truth, but in the search for it.
-Leo Tolstoy

In a previous letter, we defined prime numbers and encountered the remarkable fact that every integer can be written as the product of primes. This product is called the prime decomposition, and it is unique for each integer. To review an example, the prime decomposition of 24 is $2 \cdot 2 \cdot 2 \cdot 3$.

Why is the prime decomposition expressed using multiplication and not addition? As the first arithmetic operation learned, addition is even more fundamental than multiplication. Is there a way to quickly establish why multiplication is used over addition?

Let's experiment with an example using the number 24. Can 24 be written as a *sum* of primes? It certainly can; for example, $24 = 7 + 17$ works. However, the sums $24 = 5 + 19$ and $24 = 7 + 7 + 7 + 3$ also work. Herein lies the problem: there is more than one way to write 24 as a sum of prime numbers. The prime decomposition $24 = 2 \cdot 2 \cdot 2 \cdot 3$ has the useful property of uniqueness, but this does not hold for sums.

Although writing 24 as a sum of primes did not lead to a unique answer, a few solutions do exist. Writing a positive integer as a sum of other positive integers (not necessarily primes) is referred to as a *partition*. For example, here are the ten ways 6 can be partitioned:

$$6 = 5 + 1$$
$$6 = 4 + 2$$
$$6 = 3 + 3$$
$$6 = 4 + 1 + 1$$
$$6 = 3 + 2 + 1$$
$$6 = 2 + 2 + 2$$
$$6 = 3 + 1 + 1 + 1$$
$$6 = 2 + 2 + 1 + 1$$
$$6 = 2 + 1 + 1 + 1 + 1$$
$$6 = 1 + 1 + 1 + 1 + 1 + 1$$

The number of partitions grows rapidly for large numbers. In fact, efficiently computing how many partitions exist for a given number is not easy. Even with the advent of fast computers, it is still difficult to compute the precise number of partitions for very large integers.

In the early 1900s the brilliant Indian mathematician Srinivasa Ramanujan discovered a remarkable formula to approximate the number of partitions for any integer n:

$$\frac{e^{\pi \cdot \sqrt{\frac{2 \cdot n}{3}}}}{4 \cdot n \cdot \sqrt{3}}$$

Surprisingly, both π and e show up in the formula. It is more accurate when the integer n is large, but to give a sense of how quickly the number of partitions grow, let's try the number 100. Rounding to the nearest whole number gives:

$$\frac{e^{\pi \cdot \sqrt{\frac{2 \cdot 100}{3}}}}{4 \cdot 100 \cdot \sqrt{3}} = 199280893$$

This is only an approximation, but it is not too far off. The true answer is around 190 million, meaning that there are more than 190 million unique ways to write 100 as the sum of other positive integers; much higher than intuition might suggest.

Although partitioning an integer is an interesting area of study in its own right, our focus will be on prime partitions. Notice that of the partitions for 6, two of them contain only primes: they are $6 = 3 + 3$ and $6 = 2 + 2 + 2$. For 8, a bit of trial and error shows that it can be written as the sum of primes $8 = 5 + 3$. This is not the only way to do it; it can also be written as the sum of primes $8 = 2 + 2 + 2 + 2$. How about 10? It can be written as $10 = 5 + 5$, $10 = 7 + 3$, or $10 = 2 + 2 + 2 + 2 + 2$ to name a few.

In all of the examples so far there has been at least one way to write the number as the sum of only two primes:

$$24 = 5 + 19 \ (\text{and } 7 + 17)$$
$$6 = 3 + 3$$
$$8 = 3 + 5$$
$$10 = 5 + 5 \ (\text{and } 7 + 3)$$

Can every integer be written as the sum of only *two* prime numbers? The answer to this question is no, but for a rather mundane reason. Recall that a prime number is by definition only divisible by 1 and itself. Therefore, with the exception of 2, all primes must be odd. It is easy to see why—every even integer is divisible by 2.

The consequence of this fact is that when two primes are summed, save for the special case of the number 2, both numbers will be odd. The sum of two odd numbers is always an even number. For example, $7 + 3$ is the even number 10, and $5 + 3$ is the even number 8; two odd quantities always combine to make an even quantity.

If all integers cannot be written as the sum of two primes, then how about just the even integers? This seems a bit more promising, and leads to one of the greatest unsolved problems in mathematics.

Originally proposed in the mid 1700s, *Goldbach's conjecture* is named after the German mathematician Christian Goldbach.

The conjecture states:

Every even integer greater than 2 can be written as the sum of two primes.

While there may be more than one way to do it, the conjecture states that there is always *at least* one way. Below are a few more examples:

$$18 = 5 + 13$$
$$30 = 11 + 19$$
$$38 = 7 + 31$$
$$54 = 13 + 41$$
$$100 = 97 + 3$$

Despite considerable effort through the centuries, no one has been able to prove the conjecture. Computers have been used to test millions of integers, but this does not constitute a proof. A monstrous even integer might exist that *cannot* be written as the sum of two primes.

Goldbach's conjecture is famous for many of the same reasons as the Collatz conjecture, which was covered in a previous letter. Although the two problems are very different, their fame is widespread because 1) they can be understood by nearly everyone and 2) despite considerable effort, they have remained unsolved for decades. This is even more astonishing considering the fact that Goldbach's conjecture is over 250 years old—more than twice the age of the Collatz conjecture.

One way to think about Goldbach's conjecture is to imagine an infinite grid, a snippet of which appears below:

	2	3	5	7	11
2	4	5	7	9	13
3	5	6	8	10	14
5	7	8	10	12	16
7	9	10	12	14	18
11	13	14	16	18	22

The prime numbers are written along the top, and then again down the left side. The interior of the grid contains the sum of each pair of prime numbers. For instance, the number 12 located in the 3rd row and 4th column is the sum of the primes 7 from the top and 5 from the left. The grid is symmetric around the diagonal because the ordering of terms in a sum does not matter—$7 + 5$ is the same as $5 + 7$. Due to this fact, we really only need to compute either the top or bottom diagonal half of the grid.

The even numbers $4, 6, 8, 10, 12, 14, 16$ all appear at least once within the grid. Goldbach's conjecture implies that every even integer larger than 2 will occur at least once *somewhere* in this grid as it expands. That is of course if the conjecture is true.

When faced with thorny problems like Goldbach's conjecture, mathematicians will often try to tease out useful visual patterns. Unexpected patterns appearing in plots can sometimes lead to ideas not readily discernible in the numbers alone. This is a good strategy to keep in mind when facing any quantitative problem.

There is one plot of particular interest connected with Goldbach's conjecture. It concerns the *number* of different ways each even integer can be written as the sum of two primes. To illustrate, here are the different ways the first few even integers can be written as the sum of two primes:

$$4 = 2 + 2$$
$$6 = 3 + 3$$
$$8 = 3 + 5$$
$$10 = 3 + 7 \text{ and } 5 + 5$$

The integers 4, 6, and 8 can only be written as the sum of two primes in one way; 10, on the other hand, can be written in two distinct ways. As the integer increases, there are more ways to write it as the sum of two primes. For instance, there are three ways to write 22: $3 + 19$, $5 + 17$, and $11 + 11$.

Let's create a plot with even integers on the horizontal axis and the number of ways each can be written as the sum of two primes on the vertical axis. The first few points for the even integers 4, 6, 8, and 10 look like this:

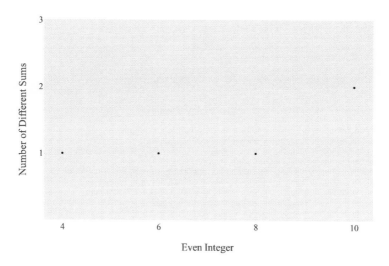

Number of Ways to Write Even Integer as the Sum of 2 Primes

Now we'll fill in the plot for every even integer up to 25000.

118

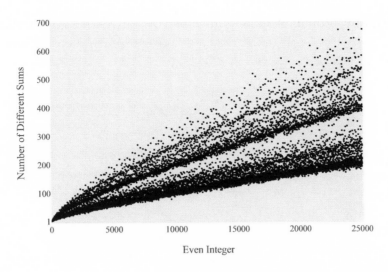

Number of Ways to Write Even Integer as the Sum of 2 Primes

This image is referred to as *Goldbach's comet*. Needless to say, it resembles the tail of a comet—with distinct dense bands flowing away across the plot. It is surprising that such an orderly picture emerges; the steady slope and dense bands are unexpected. Interestingly, for Goldbach's conjecture to be false, there must be a point that falls to 0 somewhere in the infinite tail of this comet; meaning that there are 0 ways to write the integer as the sum of two primes.

The mysterious bands in the comet are significant, and they suggest a subtle connection between the form of certain even integers and the number of ways they can be written as the sum of two primes. For example, even multiples of 3 share a similar growth rate in the plot, clustering into the same band. Even multiples of 5 and 7 cluster into their own bands as well. Exploring *why* this is the case would lead us too far astray, but it is apparent that Goldbach's conjecture reveals unforeseen patterns between different groups of integers. Unfortunately, this information has not helped in the quest to prove the conjecture.

An interesting phenomenon with unsolved conjectures is that slight variations can produce superficially similar problems. Even though the altered problem may seem similar to the original, the approach to a solution may be radically different. While not always the case, mathematicians are sometimes able to produce a solution for the altered problem. This occurred with what is known as Goldbach's *weak* conjecture. The conjecture states:

Every odd integer greater than 5 can be expressed as the sum of three primes.

This conjecture has the same flavor as the original. The main difference is that it calls for *three* prime numbers instead of two. Since all primes except for 2 are odd, most sums will consist of three odd numbers. When three odd numbers are summed the result is another odd number. Therefore, the second major difference is that this conjecture applies to all the *odd* integers greater than 5.

Here are some examples:

$$9 = 3 + 3 + 3$$
$$11 = 3 + 3 + 5$$
$$13 = 3 + 3 + 7 \ \ (\text{and } 3 + 5 + 5)$$
$$15 = 3 + 5 + 7 \ \ (\text{and } 5 + 5 + 5)$$

Unlike Goldbach's original conjecture, this one has been proven. The proof was offered relatively recently in 2013 by the Peruvian mathematician Harald Helfgott. The slight switch from two primes to three changed the dynamics of the problem just enough to admit a proof.

Goldbach's conjecture endures as one of the oldest and most famous unsolved problems in mathematics; stumping some of the greatest minds for over two centuries. It is all the more captivating because similar problems, like Goldbach's weak conjecture, have been solved. It is widely believed that Goldbach's conjecture is also true, but that remains up for debate until a proof is discovered.

Calculus
Letter 15

Mathematics is the gate and key to the sciences.
-Roger Bacon

Calculus is one of the most useful discoveries to emerge from the field of mathematics. Although some rudimentary aspects of calculus have been known for millennia, we owe its modern development to the work of Gottfried Leibniz and Isaac Newton in the late 17th century. In their day it was hotly debated which mathematician, and therefore which country, Leibniz from Germany and Newton from England, deserved the credit. Today it is acknowledged that both men arrived at the methods independently.

College students in mathematics, physics, engineering, and many other fields typically spend their first year of study immersed in calculus. In a sense, it is the gateway to advanced study for many scientific disciplines. The overarching idea behind calculus is one of stunning simplicity and effectiveness. Unfortunately, the beauty of the subject is often obscured behind endless formulas and shortcuts.

To illustrate the types of problems that calculus solves, it is best to begin with a simple example.

Imagine a car traveling on a straight road at a constant speed. Questions regarding the direction of travel or the distance covered can be answered rather easily. For instance, if the car is traveling at 60 miles per hour, how far has it traveled after 5 hours? Well, if the speed is constant at 60 miles per hour, then after 5 hours it has traveled $60 \cdot 5 = 300$ miles. When dealing with straight lines and constant unchanging motion most calculations are easy and intuitive.

The scenario above is ideal from a calculation perspective, but it is completely unrealistic. In reality, the car's speed will constantly change and the road may be winding and hilly; the questions posed above become much more challenging to answer. Fortunately, this is where calculus shines—it is the mathematics of motion and change. Calculus allows us to answer complicated real-world questions where conditions are in constant flux.

It is not difficult to generalize the car example to other scenarios. Think of the motion of a ball or projectile through the air, the movement of orbiting planets, or the transfer of heat as it travels across a surface. The popularity of calculus stems from its ability to accurately model the kind of motion and change observed in our world.

How is calculus able to tackle such a wide array of problems? The key lies in breaking each problem down into smaller, more manageable pieces. After solving each of the smaller problems, they are reassembled into an overall solution.

Calculus works by carrying this idea to its limit. Problems are dismantled into *infinitely many small chunks*. Each piece is far less complicated than the whole, and can be dealt with accordingly. This is precisely why the concept of infinity is so crucial in calculus, but it is also the main source of confusion when first introduced. Our previous letter addressing the concept of infinity and limits will be particularly relevant in what follows.

Sticking with the car example, the total distance traveled can be visualized with a plot. The horizontal axis will be labeled with a t for time (in hours), and the vertical axis will show various speeds in miles per hour from 30 to 90. The dotted line at 60 represents the speed of the car *at each point in time*. In this case, the car is traveling at a constant 60 miles per hour, so the dotted line stays at 60 as time passes. This simple scenario is plotted below:

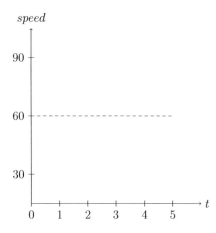

After 5 hours of driving how far has the car traveled? It turns out that the answer is exactly equal to the area under the dotted line.

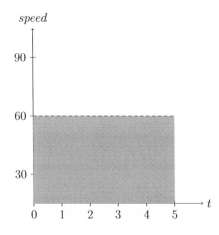

Thus, this question can be recast as a geometric problem. What if the car is not traveling at a constant speed, but rather starts off at 60, increases speed to 90, and then slows down to 30? Of course, these changes will not be abrupt as the car accelerates and decelerates, so the plot might look like the one shown next.

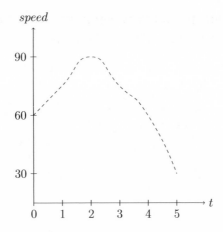

What is the total distance traveled? This is more difficult to calculate, but the geometry remains the same. The total distance traveled is given by the *area* of the shaded region:

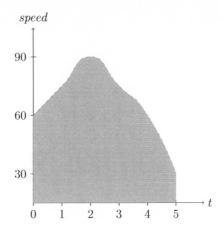

Fluctuating speed plotted as a function of time is what forces us to deal with curves, and finding the area under these curves will answer many useful questions, including the total distance traveled.

For the sake of clarity, let's demonstrate the essential idea behind calculus using a less complicated curve. Imagine a car accelerating smoothly from 0 miles per hour to some top speed, say 30 miles per hour, and then decelerating smoothly back down to 0. To keep the picture as simple as possible we will concentrate only on the curve itself, and leave off the plot axes. The speed over time might look like the idealized arc shown below:

Computing the area under this arc will give the total distance traveled. The problem is that computing the area of curved shapes is hard. Computing the area of shapes made of straight lines, on the other hand, is easy. Therefore, we will start by using simple shapes to *approximate* the area under this curve.

Rectangles are easy to deal with; they are made of straight lines, and multiplying base times height gives the area. To approximate the area under the arc let's first try two rectangles:

Without performing any computations, it is clear that the area of the two rectangles will not yield a very accurate estimate.

Let's try 4 rectangles:

This approximation is still rough, and it is obvious that the areas of all rectangles combined will be larger than the area under the arc.

Let's try 8 rectangles:

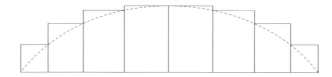

The top edges rising above the arc will throw off the approximation, but if we computed the area of each rectangle and summed them up, we would be close to the area under the curve. Now imagine continuing this process using more and more rectangles; they would become very skinny, but the area of each is easily computed.

The mental leap of faith seized on by Newton and Leibniz was to push this idea to the extreme. This is where the concept of infinity and limits come into play. Calculus treats the problem exactly as we have so far, by approximating the area using rectangles. The breakthrough is achieved when the number of rectangles goes to infinity.

In a previous letter on infinity and limits, we studied the expression $\frac{1}{n}$ and determined that the limit of this expression was 0 as n goes to infinity. Calculus uses limits in a similar way. If there is a mathematical expression approximating the area under the curve using n rectangles, then taking the limit of this expression as the number of rectangles goes to infinity miraculously results in the correct answer.

This idea is intuitive up to a point. Allowing the number of rectangles to go to infinity is certainly a mind-bending thought, but based on the pictures so far it is not so difficult to envision. What is still a bit mystifying is how this process actually works in the realm of mathematical formulas. The pictures convey the idea, but how do these translate into actual numbers? To demonstrate how infinity and limits are used to derive numerical answers, let's step through an example using numbers and formulas.

In most real-world scenarios a mathematical *function* describing some aspect of the object under study is necessary; for example, a function describing the position or the speed of an object through time. Questions concerning the direction of travel, the distance covered, or related concepts of motion will rely on the function as a starting point.

We have used functions several times in the past. For instance, x^2 and $2 \cdot x + 1$ are both functions. The symbol used as a placeholder is arbitrary—x is traditional, but if the function describes something evolving through time it is standard practice to use the letter t instead. The functions x^2 and t^2 are exactly the same; nothing more than tradition dictates which letter a particular math textbook uses as a placeholder.

There are many different functions to choose from, but t^2 will work well for our example. It is nonlinear (i.e. the plot is not a straight line) yet relatively simple. Assume that this function gives the speed of a car through time, where time is measured in hours. At hour $t = 0$ the car is traveling $0^2 = 0$ miles per hour. At hour 1 it is traveling $1^2 = 1$ miles per hour, at hour 2 it is traveling $2^2 = 4$ miles per hour, and so on. Plotting this function with time on the horizontal axis and speed on the vertical axis yields:

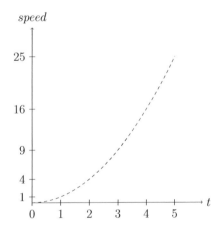

This is similar to our earlier plot for the car with constant speed 60, except now the speed evolves over time according to the function t^2.

To obtain the total distance traveled we need to find the area under this curve. As before, it can be approximated starting with two evenly spaced rectangles. It is possible to use uneven rectangles of varying widths, but there is no benefit—it only makes the math more complicated.

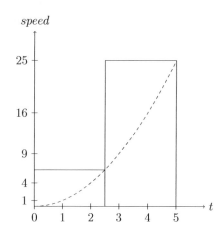

Now we must compute the area of these rectangles. The base of each measures 2.5 units; the first one spans the horizontal axis from 0 to 2.5, and the second spans 2.5 to 5. How about the heights? The upper right corners of both rectangles intersect the dashed line, so the value of the dashed line at those points will give the heights. This is where the function t^2 is useful. The dashed line is the plot of t^2, so plugging the number from the horizontal axis into this function produces the height. The first rectangle's height is $2.5^2 = 6.25$, and the second rectangle's height is $5^2 = 25$.

To compute the combined area of the rectangles simply multiply base times height for each and add them together:

$$2.5 \cdot 2.5^2 + 2.5 \cdot 5^2 = 78.125$$

This is not a great approximation, so let's try using 4 equally spaced rectangles:

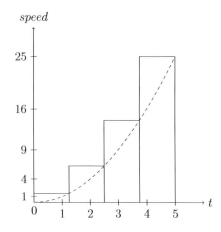

Instead of eyeballing the base lengths, let's be a bit more systematic. There is a total length of 5 units to cover on the horizontal axis. If all 4 rectangles have equal base lengths, then each one must take up one-fourth of the total 5 units. This implies a base length of $\frac{5}{4} = 1.25$ for each.

The heights can once again be determined by the function. The height of the first rectangle is $1.25^2 = 1.5625$. Moving 1.25 more units to the right lands us at the right edge of the second rectangle, or $1.25 + 1.25 = 2.5$ on the horizontal axis. Plugging in 2.5 gives a height of $2.5^2 = 6.25$ for the second rectangle. Continuing on like this we have a height of $3.75^2 =$

14.0625 for the third rectangle and a height of $5^2 = 25$ for the fourth. Using the same base times height formula for each rectangle their combined areas come out to:

$$1.25 \cdot 1.25^2 + 1.25 \cdot 2.5^2 + 1.25 \cdot 3.75^2 + 1.25 \cdot 5^2 = 58.59375$$

While this approximation is closer, there is still a lot of slack where the rectangles go above the dashed curve.

Here is one final picture using 8 rectangles:

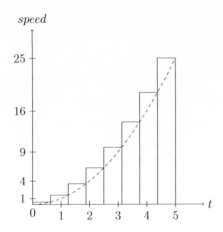

There are 8 equally spaced rectangles taking up 5 units in total. The base of each must be $\frac{5}{8} = .625$ units long, and traveling along the horizontal axis in steps of .625 will give the heights by plugging each number into the function t^2. In the interest of space we will not write out the full computation, but the final sum of areas comes out to 49.805 rounded to three decimal places.

These computations are becoming tedious. Mathematics revolves around leveraging general patterns to make calculations easier, and this is especially true in calculus.

Instead of choosing a specific number of rectangles, let's think more abstractly. Suppose there are n rectangles. The case for n equal to 2, 4, and 8 have already been worked out. When there are n equally spaced rectangles the base of each measures $\frac{5}{n}$ units ($n = 2$ was $\frac{5}{2} = 2.5$, $n = 4$ was $\frac{5}{4} = 1.25$, and $n = 8$ was $\frac{5}{8} = .625$) In other words, the general formula $\frac{5}{n}$ is the base length of each rectangle when there are n of them.

What about the heights? Notice that computing the heights is equivalent to moving down the horizontal axis in steps equal to the base length, and plugging the numbers into the function t^2. For example, with $n = 4$ the base length was $\frac{5}{4} = 1.25$ units. To compute the heights we moved to the points:

$$1.25, 2.50, 3.75, 5$$

along the horizontal axis and plugged them into the function. The key is to realize that this sequence can be rewritten as:

$$1 \cdot 1.25, 2 \cdot 1.25, 3 \cdot 1.25, 4 \cdot 1.25$$

Think of the multipliers 1, 2, 3, 4 as the number of "steps" taken down the horizontal axis; each step moves 1.25 additional units to the right, and lands at the right edge of the next rectangle.

Keeping with the abstract notion of n rectangles, this means that taking steps of size $\frac{5}{n}$ (the base length) along the horizontal axis will land exactly at the right edge of each rectangle:

$$1 \cdot \frac{5}{n}, 2 \cdot \frac{5}{n}, 3 \cdot \frac{5}{n}, ..., n \cdot \frac{5}{n}$$

The ellipsis stands in for all the points between $3 \cdot \frac{5}{n}$ and the last point, $n \cdot \frac{5}{n}$. For example, plugging $n = 4$ into this expression gives the sequence of points for the case of 4 rectangles:

$$1 \cdot \frac{5}{4}, 2 \cdot \frac{5}{4}, 3 \cdot \frac{5}{4}, 4 \cdot \frac{5}{4}$$

Written in decimal form the above is equal to:

$$1 \cdot 1.25, 2 \cdot 1.25, 3 \cdot 1.25, 4 \cdot 1.25$$

which we arrived at previously.

Plugging the sequence of numbers above into the function t^2 yields the heights. For the case of n rectangles the heights are:

$$\left(1 \cdot \frac{5}{n}\right)^2, \left(2 \cdot \frac{5}{n}\right)^2, \left(3 \cdot \frac{5}{n}\right)^2, ..., \left(n \cdot \frac{5}{n}\right)^2$$

The next step is to use the (base) $\cdot$ (height) formula to find the area of each rectangle and add them all up. Using the two general expressions above ($\frac{5}{n}$ for the base length and the sequence of heights) this comes out to:

$$\left(\frac{5}{n}\right) \cdot \left(1 \cdot \frac{5}{n}\right)^2 + \left(\frac{5}{n}\right) \cdot \left(2 \cdot \frac{5}{n}\right)^2 + \left(\frac{5}{n}\right) \cdot \left(3 \cdot \frac{5}{n}\right)^2 + ... + \left(\frac{5}{n}\right) \cdot \left(n \cdot \frac{5}{n}\right)^2$$

The beauty of this expression is that it works for *any* number n of equally spaced rectangles on the plot.

Each term in the preceding addition represents the area of one rectangle. These are precisely the small sub-problems alluded to earlier. Each sub-problem is an easy computation, and summing them together yields an approximation for the area under the curve of the function t^2 from 0 to 5.

To check this expression using a few concrete examples, plug in $n = 2$ to get:

$$\left(\frac{5}{2}\right) \cdot \left(1 \cdot \frac{5}{2}\right)^2 + \left(\frac{5}{2}\right) \cdot \left(2 \cdot \frac{5}{2}\right)^2 = 78.125$$

This is precisely the area computed previously using 2 rectangles. When $n = 4$ the answer is:

$$\left(\frac{5}{4}\right) \cdot \left(1 \cdot \frac{5}{4}\right)^2 + \left(\frac{5}{4}\right) \cdot \left(2 \cdot \frac{5}{4}\right)^2 + \left(\frac{5}{4}\right) \cdot \left(3 \cdot \frac{5}{4}\right)^2 + \left(\frac{5}{4}\right) \cdot \left(4 \cdot \frac{5}{4}\right)^2 = 58.59375$$

Again, this matches the area computed previously using 4 rectangles. This abstract expression translates our pictures into numbers.

The final step, and this is where the true magic of calculus occurs, is to ask what happens as n goes to infinity. This can be expressed in symbols. Using the limit notation from an earlier letter on infinity and limits:

$$\lim_{n\to\infty} \left(\left(\frac{5}{n}\right) \cdot \left(1 \cdot \frac{5}{n}\right)^2 + \left(\frac{5}{n}\right) \cdot \left(2 \cdot \frac{5}{n}\right)^2 + \left(\frac{5}{n}\right) \cdot \left(3 \cdot \frac{5}{n}\right)^2 + ... + \left(\frac{5}{n}\right) \cdot \left(n \cdot \frac{5}{n}\right)^2 \right) = ?$$

Asking what happens as n goes to infinity is equivalent to asking what happens as the number of rectangles goes to infinity. In fact, this expression represents an infinite sum, and the number of terms grows as n grows.

The amazing result is that as n goes to infinity, this expression *does* converge to a single number—it has a limit. That limit is:

$$\frac{125}{3} = 41.667$$

rounded to three decimal places. A car with a speed function of t^2 would have traveled a distance of 41.667 miles by hour 5.

We can watch the limit emerge numerically as n grows. Writing out each sum in its entirety would take up too much space, so we will settle for a table that starts with the example values (2, 4, and 8) and then grows more rapidly:

n	Final Sum
2	78.125
4	58.594
8	49.805
10	48.125
100	42.294
1000	41.729
10000	41.673
100000	41.667

The last row is the area under the curve of the function t^2 from 0 to 5 rounded to three decimal places if it was estimated using 100000 tiny rectangles.

Many calculus books contain shortcut formulas to find the area under the curve of common functions like t^2. This partly explains why these books are filled with so many formulas; most of them are shortcuts to avoid working through the true underlying calculations.

Finding the area under a curve corresponds to the idea of an *integral* in calculus, and it is one of the core pillars of the subject. Although we didn't show an example, there is a closely related concept that deals directly with the curves themselves. Curves are dealt with in a similar way, by breaking them into infinitely many shapes that are easier to understand. Evaluating the area required two-dimensional rectangles, but for one-dimensional curves, tiny straight lines are used. This idea corresponds to the concept of a *derivative* in calculus. Integrals and derivatives are closely related, and they both rely on the same crucial idea of breaking each problem down into infinitely many small pieces. It is astonishing that this scheme actually works, and the advent of calculus has allowed scientists to solve countless problems which, prior to its discovery, were simply insurmountable.

The Normal Distribution

Letter 16

It is not certain that everything is uncertain.
-Blaise Pascal

The field of *statistics* strives to create order from randomness. While this may seem rather counterintuitive, if the same random event occurs with enough frequency, a surprising amount of information can be gleaned.

To illustrate, consider the following scenario: suppose a bet is offered based on a single coin toss. If it lands heads up we win a dollar, but if it lands tails up we lose a dollar. Is this a good bet? Probably not, since the odds of winning or losing are the same. Now, what if the bet was changed to reflect the *number* of heads that occur in 100 tosses of a coin? Assume we win a dollar if the number of heads is between 40 and 60, and lose a dollar otherwise. Is this a better bet? The ultimate outcome is still random, but the *probability* of winning a dollar seems skewed in our favor; with a fair coin, the number of heads should be around 50, and this is well within the bounds of 40 and 60. Therefore, it is probably a decent bet to take.

The key insight is that although a single event may be random, aggregating many of these events together can lead to rather precise predictions.

Let's explore the coin tossing example in more detail by considering 10 hypothetical tosses as shown in the table below. Each row of the table represents a separate toss. The outcome of each toss appears in the Heads or Tails column, a running total of heads in the Total Heads column, and the proportion of heads in the Proportion of Heads column. Take a moment to inspect the table:

Toss	Heads or Tails	Total Heads	Proportion of Heads
1	T	0	0
2	T	0	0
3	T	0	0
4	T	0	0
5	H	1	.20
6	H	2	.33
7	T	2	.29
8	T	2	.25
9	T	2	.22
10	T	2	.20

The first four tosses yield tails (T), followed by two heads (H) in a row. Total Heads is incremented by 1 at toss 5 and then again at toss 6. After 4 more tosses come up tails, the Total Heads count of 2 is carried forward without incrementing.

The Proportion of Heads is calculated by dividing the Total Heads column by the Toss column. While there is no way to predict the outcome per toss, the proportion running down the right column *can* be predicted—it should approach .5 as the tosses continue.

The first and last columns of this table can be visualized using a plot. The horizontal axis represents the number of tosses, and the vertical axis displays the proportion of heads. The plot corresponding to the table looks like this:

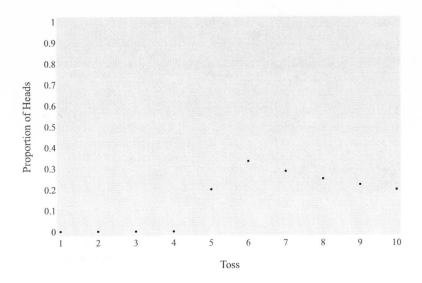

Proportion of Heads for 10 Tosses

Increasing the number of tosses from 10 to 100 would result in a plot similar to the one shown next:

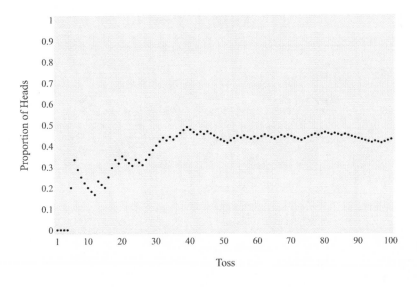

Proportion of Heads for 100 Tosses

The proportion of heads is volatile at first, but settles down dramatically beyond 20 or so tosses. Near the end of the 100 tosses the proportion hovers close to .5 as expected.

This plot shows that the proportion of heads gradually loses its randomness. The principle governing this loss of randomness is the same principle leveraged by casinos and is known as the *Law of Large Numbers*. Although each slot machine may only have a 60% chance of earning the casino a profit, they are bound to come out ahead if hundreds of people are playing. Each machine can be viewed as a biased coin, and each pull on the lever is like a toss. In the long run the win rate for the casino will be close to precisely 60%, earning them a profit.

The main idea is that when many random events are aggregated, the end result gradually becomes more reliable. Another way to think about this is to imagine each random event as a small piece of information. By itself, this piece of information is not very useful. However, when many small pieces of information are combined, the randomness diminishes, and the information content grows.

There is one important aspect we have yet to address in the coin toss example, and that is the *variance* expected in the proportion of heads. The variance is a measure of uncertainty, and it can be observed in the plots as the points whipsaw in the beginning before ultimately settling down near .5. With only a few tosses the true proportion of heads is not certain (maybe the coin is biased), but after nearly 100 tosses the proportion of heads has settled near .5 and the uncertainty decreases. Another term often used for this same idea is the *standard deviation*, which is closely related to the variance (it is actually the square root of the variance).

A key focus in the field of statistics is deriving a *probability distribution* (or just *distribution* for short) which closely models the outcome of a given random process. Notably, the distribution takes into account the variance associated with an outcome. The way statisticians think about the distribution of a random event offers a new and useful way of thinking.

To introduce distributions, let's first focus on the plot of 100 coin tosses. This is only *one* realization of 100 coin tosses. If we recorded another 100 tosses, the plot would likely be different. For instance, here are 2 more plots showing the proportion of heads for 100 coin tosses.

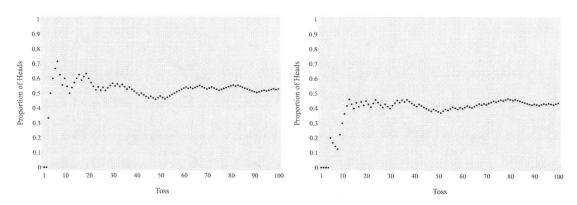

Proportion of Heads for 100 Tosses   Proportion of Heads for 100 Tosses

The plots eventually settle near .5, but the paths, as well as the final proportion of heads, are slightly different. The last point on the left plot sits at .53, while the plot on the right ends with a proportion of .44.

By repeating the same experiment over and over, the variability of the end result can be assessed. Thinking back to the earlier betting problem, this helps us judge the *probability* of ending between 40 and 60 heads after 100 tosses.

Similar to the two plots above, we will simulate 100 tosses of a coin 8 more times, but only record the ending proportion of heads. We'll use a table to organize the results, and the previous two trials will make up the first two rows:

Trial	Number of Tosses	Final Proportion of Heads
1	100	.53
2	100	.44
3	100	.47
4	100	.56
5	100	.53
6	100	.49
7	100	.44
8	100	.47
9	100	.40
10	100	.53

This table offers a simple method to record results, but it is difficult to appreciate the information as it expands to many thousands of rows. To attain a better understanding of the data a common statistical plot known as a *histogram* will be used.

Histograms are the tool of choice for visualizing probability distributions. In this case, the distribution of interest is the final proportion of heads after 100 tosses of a fair coin. A histogram resembles a bar chart. The horizontal axis will list the proportion of heads, and the height of each bar corresponds to *how many times* that proportion was observed.

To demonstrate, here is the histogram for the 10 row table above:

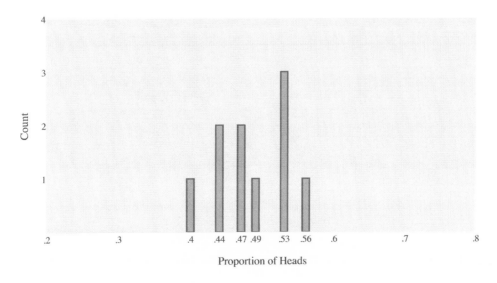

Histogram for 10 Trials

The first bar, located at .4 on the horizontal axis, has a height of 1. This is because the proportion .4 only occurred in one trial (Trial 9). Likewise, the bars above .49 and .56 have heights of 1 because these proportions were only observed once in the table. Lastly, the bars above both .44 and .47 have a height of 2, and the bar above .53 has a height of 3, since these proportions were observed 2 and 3 times respectively.

In brief, a histogram gives a sense of how likely an outcome is to occur—the more frequent an outcome, the higher the bar for that value. Noticeably, there are no bars to the left of .4 or to the right of .56 since these proportions never occurred in the trials.

To gather more data we can perform more trials of 100 tosses each, in essence extending the table to thousands of rows and filling in the histogram. The result for 15000 total trials is shown next:

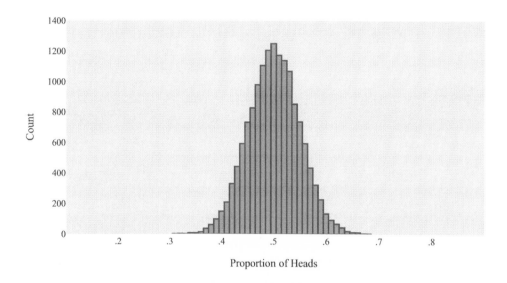

Histogram for 15000 Trials

A remarkably well-defined bell shape emerges! Even though the outcome of each trial is random, in aggregate they certainly seem to follow a pattern. The highest bars are clustered around .5 as expected, and the lack of bars below approximately .3 or above .7 are also intuitive—it would be rare to observe outcomes as extreme as below 30% or above 70% heads after 100 tosses of a fair coin.

The histogram provides something that the earlier plots did not: not only is the most likely final outcome obvious, but the variance of the outcomes is readily apparent as well. The histogram offers a complete picture, and gives all the information necessary to answer probabilistic questions. If we want to know the approximate probability of observing a proportion of heads between .4 and .6 after 100 tosses, we can add up the heights of all bars between .4 and .6, which turns out to be 14462. Dividing this by the total number of trials, 15000, yields $\frac{14462}{15000} = .96$ rounded to two decimal places. Therefore, the probability of ending with a proportion of heads between .4 and .6 after 100 tosses is approximately 96%.

There is only one problem with this histogram—its creation required 15000 coin toss simulations. If another 15000 trials were simulated, the resulting histogram would be slightly different, and any computations based on the histogram would vary as well. The 96% probability computed above might turn out to be 95% if based on another simulated histogram. The answers will be close, but there will still be some variation. Instead of empirically creating the histogram, it would be nice to have a compact formula that represents it.

Let's take another look at the histogram. It seems to follow a curve like the one outlined below:

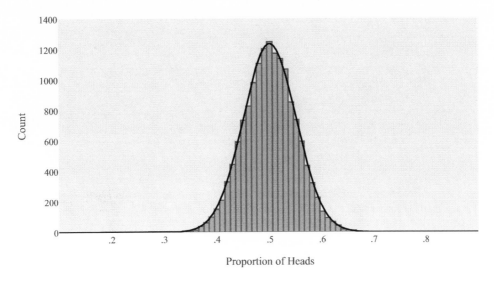

Histogram for 15000 Trials with Approximating Curve

Amazingly, this curve is not arbitrary; rather, it is a scaled version of one of the most important functions in all of statistics. This function is known by several names including the *normal distribution*, the *bell curve*, and the *Gaussian distribution*. The latter name is in honor of the famous German mathematician Carl Friedrich Gauss who discovered and studied the curve in the early 19th century.

If the number of trials was increased beyond 15000 the resulting histogram would approximate the curve even better. The normal distribution is so fascinating because it arises in countless scenarios far beyond simple coin tossing.

Consider the following histograms consisting of real-world data. The first shows the weights of 5000 adult males, the second shows the heights of 5000 adult females, and the last shows 10 years of daily stock returns from the S&P 500 index. In each case a scaled version of the normal distribution is drawn on top of the histogram. The fit is not perfect, but the bell shape clearly emerges in each plot.

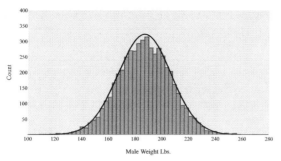
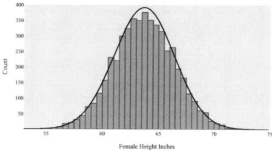

Histogram of Adult Male Weight   Histogram of Adult Female Height

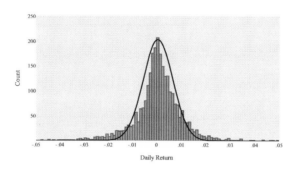

Histogram of S&P 500 Daily Returns

Some curves are wider or taller than others, but they are all *scaled* versions of the same underlying curve. This is similar to scaling a shape, like the sides of a rectangle. A rectangle with side lengths 1 and 2 has a different appearance than a rectangle with sides 5 and 20, but the essence of the underlying shape is the same—they are both rectangles. The bell curve works in a similar manner. It can be scaled up or down, made wide or narrow, but these are all variations of the same underlying curve.

The prevalence of the bell curve can be explained by an extraordinary theorem in statistics known as the *Central Limit Theorem*. The theorem roughly states that when an outcome is the result of many small, independent contributions, then its probability distribution will approximately follow the bell curve.

This is certainly true in the coin tossing example. Each toss of the coin contributes a small independent piece of information to the final proportion of heads after 100 tosses. How about the height and weight of a person? Both of these metrics can be viewed as the outcome of various genetic and environmental factors, each one playing a small role in the final height and weight. The same can be said of stock market returns, which are the culmination of many small independent forces that push prices up or down each day.

This also explains why the normal distribution is so prevalent in nature. Just like height and weight, most natural processes are the result of many small independent contributions from the surrounding environment. For example, at the risk of oversimplifying, an apple is the aggregate result of changing weather over many months. Each day contributes a small amount to the overall size of the final apple, and if we tabulated the size of 10000 apples, the resulting histogram would likely follow a bell curve.

The normal distribution has connections to several other areas of mathematics. One surprising connection is to a structure we have studied in the past—Pascal's triangle.

To quickly review, recall that each number in Pascal's triangle is computed by summing the two numbers above it. The next picture shows several rows of the triangle. Below each number is a small black dot, and each number in the last row is enclosed in a small box. We will explain this setup in a moment.

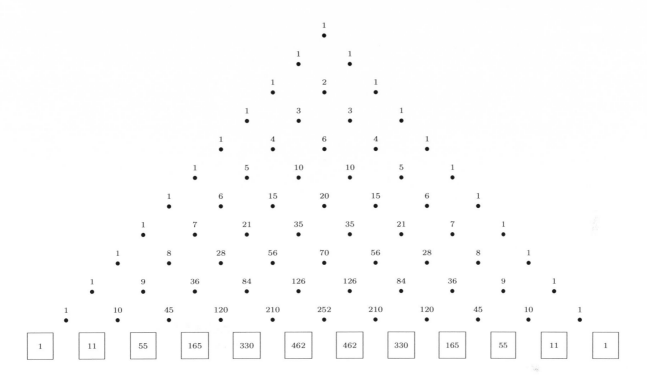

Think of the small dots as nails sticking out from a vertical board, and the boxes at the bottom as small bins. Suppose we let a ping pong ball drop onto the very first nail and watch it randomly bounce down the board. In the end, it will fall into one of the bins at the bottom. This is similar in spirit to the "plinko" board popularized on the American game show *The Price is Right*.

There are two extraordinary facts about this setup. The first is that the numbers in the bottom row of Pascal's triangle give the exact probability (or frequency) for a ball to end up in that bin. To arrive at the probability for a particular bin, divide its number by the total sum of the entire bottom row. The total sum of the bottom row is 2048, so the probability that the ball lands in the leftmost bucket labeled 462 is $\frac{462}{2048} = .2256$. In other words, after the ball randomly bounces down the pegs it has a 22.56% chance of landing in the first bucket labeled 462. What is the probability that it lands in the bucket on the left labeled 55? It is $\frac{55}{2048} = .0269$ or 2.69%. Of course, the chance of landing in the right bucket labeled 55 is 2.69% as well.

Remember that Pascal's triangle technically goes on forever. The size above was chosen to fit nicely on the page, but this property holds regardless of the triangle's size. In every case, the exact probabilities for a ball to land in a given bin can be computed directly from the bottom row. This is quite amazing considering the simple construction of the triangle; there is no reason to expect such a curious property to emerge.

The second interesting fact, and the reason for mentioning Pascal's triangle in the first place, is that it can be used to generate the normal distribution. If thousands of ping pong balls were dropped down the imaginary board they would create a natural histogram at the base, and it would closely resemble the bell curve.

One way to understand this phenomenon is to relate it to the coin toss example. Each time a ball hits a pin it has a 50/50 chance of bouncing left or right. Bouncing left can be thought of as "tails" and bouncing right as "heads". The bins at the bottom stand in for the final proportion of heads (one bin for each possible proportion). The leftmost bin with the label 1 at the bottom of the triangle represents 11 tails in a row (since there are 11 rows). The next bin to the right represents 1 head and 10 tails and so on. If the triangle had 100 rows it would be a precise replica of our earlier coin toss experiment. A single ball dropped down the board would be analogous to a single trial of 100 tosses.

There is one last unexpected secret that the normal distribution holds, and it resides within the function itself. The standard bell curve function is shown below:

$$\frac{1}{\sqrt{2 \cdot \pi}} \cdot e^{-\frac{x^2}{2}}$$

As usual, the symbol x is a placeholder for any number. The $\frac{1}{\sqrt{2 \cdot \pi}}$ piece is just a constant approximately equal to .4. The $e^{-\frac{x^2}{2}}$ piece is the special number e raised to the power $-\frac{x^2}{2}$. The incredible detail here is that the famous numbers π and e both show up in the formula. We know that π is the area of a circle with radius 1 and $e = 2.718...$ is the special irrational number encountered in an earlier letter on growth rates. By some twist of mathematical fate, both the area of a circle and continuous growth play a significant role in the bell curve.

The bell curve can be viewed as a type of *limit*. Thinking back to the letter on infinity and limits, the limit represents what happens if a process is continued indefinitely. The concept of a limit can be very abstract, and in this case we have convergence to a *function*. For example, we saw that the histogram of the coin tossing experiment lined up almost exactly with the bell curve after thousands of trials. Many random processes in fields from physics and engineering, to medicine and biology, happen to have the normal distribution as their limit.

The normal distribution is arguably the most essential distribution in statistics, and it is extremely useful for modeling real-world processes where randomness plays a role. That being said, it is not a catch-all solution for creating accurate predictions. The daily stock market return histogram is proof of this. While the bell curve approximately fits, there are many outliers in the "tails" where the histogram rises above the curve, suggesting that these events (large negative or positive returns) occur more often than the normal distribution would suggest. Nonetheless, it works well for many natural random processes, and perhaps most insightful of all, the bell curve shows that randomness can produce orderly patterns under the right conditions.

The Pythagorean Theorem
Letter 17

One cannot understand...the universality of laws of nature, the relationship of things, without an understanding of mathematics. There is no other way to do it.
-Richard P. Feynman

The Pythagorean theorem is one of the oldest, and most well known theorems of all time. It describes a remarkable relationship between the side lengths of any right triangle. Given a right triangle with sides a, b, and c:

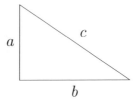

the Pythagorean theorem tells us that:

$$c^2 = a^2 + b^2$$

As long as 2 sides of the triangle are known, the third side can always be computed using this formula.

Some geometric formulas can be deduced rather easily using intuition, like the area of the right triangle above. In this case, stacking two right triangles creates a rectangle—a shape whose area is easy to compute.

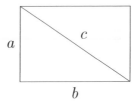

The formula for the area of a rectangle is length times width, so the area of the entire rectangle above is simply $a \cdot b$. From the picture it is clear that this formula encompasses the area of both triangles, so the area of the original triangle must be half of this, or $\frac{a \cdot b}{2}$.

Unfortunately, geometric formula derivations are not always this easy. Although the Pythagorean theorem is drilled into the heads of school children all over the world, it is not immediately clear *why* it is true, or how to derive it.

Let's consider a number x and think of what happens geometrically when that number is squared. This is not hard to envision, and the phrase "to square" a number almost gives it away. Given a line segment of length x, the quantity x^2 represents the square region enclosed by that line:

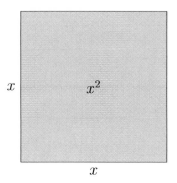

Using this geometric fact, the Pythagorean theorem can be visualized like this:

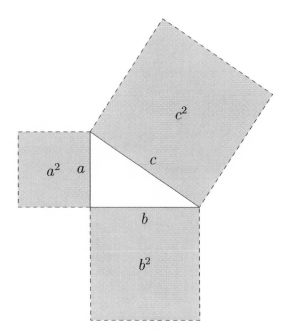

The theorem states that adding together the areas of the two smaller squares, a^2 and b^2, is equal to the area of the larger square, c^2. Given that the theorem concerns *lengths* rather than *areas*, this visual may seem strange; nonetheless, it is one valid geometric representation of the theorem.

Unlike the area of a right triangle, where it is simple to see why the formula $\frac{a \cdot b}{2}$ is true, it is not exactly obvious why the a^2 and b^2 pieces should sum to precisely c^2.

Although the picture above is technically correct, it does not give much insight. To generate a more informative graphic we'll use a trick similar to the one used earlier to find the area of a right triangle. Envision 4 identical copies of the triangle. For reference, the side length labels a, b and c will stay on the original, but will be left off the others:

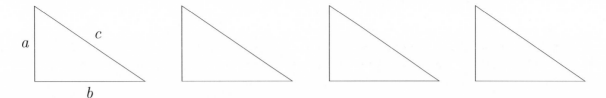

The next step is to arrange these 4 triangles in a clever way. If they are positioned in a pinwheel pattern the result is a perfect square with a small hole in the middle.

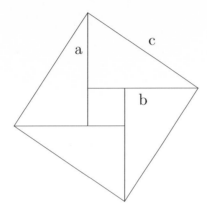

If you are skeptical that such an arrangement can be made, try it for yourself by cutting 4 identical right triangles out of paper.

This square of triangles is the key to understanding the Pythagorean theorem, and it can be used to algebraically derive the theorem from scratch. To achieve this, we will begin by assembling two different expressions for the area of this square.

First, notice that the square has side length c. Therefore, the total area of the square (including the hole in the center) is:
$$c^2$$

Now let's compute the area in a different way. From earlier, we know that the area of each triangle is $\frac{a \cdot b}{2}$. There are 4 triangles, so the total area of the 4 triangles is:

$$4 \cdot \frac{a \cdot b}{2}$$

This expression almost captures the total area of the large square, but the hole in the center is missing. In order to compute the area of the center square, we need to find its side length.

Take a moment to consider the sides of the triangles bordering the small square in the center. The length outlined by the bracket in the next picture is b.

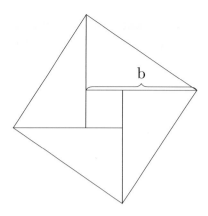

Likewise, the length outlined by the bracket below is a.

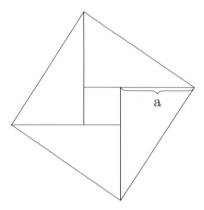

Using these two pieces of information, the side length of the small square must be $b - a$:

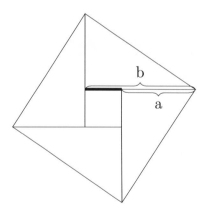

Therefore, the area of the small center square is $(b - a)^2 = (b - a) \cdot (b - a)$.

The expression $(b - a) \cdot (b - a)$ can be multiplied out using the FOIL method:

$$(b - a) \cdot (b - a) = b \cdot b - b \cdot a - a \cdot b + a \cdot a$$
$$= b^2 - 2 \cdot a \cdot b + a^2$$

We now know the area of the small center square; adding it to the area of the 4 triangles will produce the total area of the big square. This leads to:

$$\left(4 \cdot \frac{a \cdot b}{2}\right) + \left(b^2 - 2 \cdot a \cdot b + a^2\right)$$

The first term gives the area of the 4 triangles, whereas the second term is the area of the small interior square $(b - a)^2$ after rewriting using the FOIL method.

Since we have two different expressions for the area of the large square, the first being c^2, and since they are both computing the *same* area, they must be equal to one another:

$$c^2 = 4 \cdot \frac{a \cdot b}{2} + b^2 - 2 \cdot a \cdot b + a^2$$

Notice that $4 \cdot \frac{a \cdot b}{2}$ simplifies by division to $2 \cdot a \cdot b$ so the above can be rewritten as:

$$c^2 = 2 \cdot a \cdot b + b^2 - 2 \cdot a \cdot b + a^2$$

The two terms $2 \cdot a \cdot b$ and $-2 \cdot a \cdot b$ cancel each other, leaving only:

$$c^2 = a^2 + b^2$$

This is the Pythagorean theorem! The truth of the theorem is not visually obvious, yet we were able to derive it using the picture to guide our algebra.

In summary, the visual:

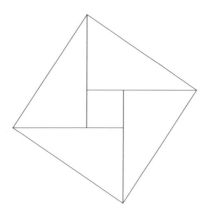

can be used to unlock the Pythagorean theorem using geometry and algebra.

Let's change focus from geometry and take a moment to consider the algebraic equation itself:

$$c^2 = a^2 + b^2$$

This relationship holds for any right triangle, and once 2 of the sides are fixed, the equation dictates the length of the third side. For instance, if a right triangle has sides $a = 1$ and $b = 2$ then the third side length c must satisfy the equation:

$$1^2 + 2^2 = c^2$$

In this case c must solve $5 = c^2$, so the third side length is $\sqrt{5} = 2.236....$

What if two sides are fixed at 2 and 3? Then the third side must have length $\sqrt{13} = 3.605....$ Or how about two sides of 6 and 10? Then the third side must have length $\sqrt{136} = 11.661....$ This leads to a rather simple but intriguing question: can a right triangle have three *integer* side lengths? For this to be true, two of the side lengths must equal a perfect square when squared and summed together. Is this possible?

The answer is yes, and it does not take much effort to find one. The side lengths $3, 4$, and 5 work because $3^2 + 4^2 = 5^2$.

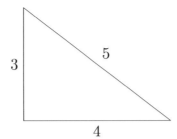

Are there others? Yes, in fact there are infinitely many. One easy way to generate them is to scale the triangle above. As an example, all sides can be multiplied by 2, therefore producing the right triangle shown below:

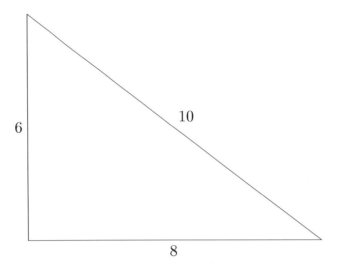

This works because multiplying all numbers in the equation by a constant does not change its validity. There are many other original combinations that work (i.e. not simply scaled versions of 3, 4, and 5), some of which are listed below:

$$5, 12, 13$$
$$8, 15, 17$$
$$7, 24, 25$$
$$20, 21, 29$$
$$12, 35, 37$$

Notice that once a and b are chosen the third number c is fixed since it must equal $\sqrt{a^2 + b^2}$. Therefore, only the first two numbers in each triple are necessary to identify it. We can visualize them in a plot with a on the horizontal axis and b on the vertical axis. There will be a point at each integer coordinate (a, b) that qualifies. For example, there will be points at $(3, 4), (5, 12), (8, 15), (7, 24)$, and so on. Here is the plot for integers up to 5000:

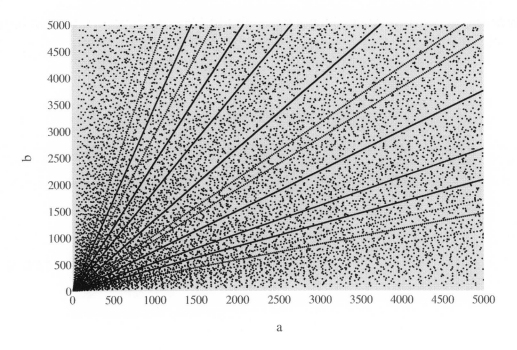

Integer Solutions a and b

Notable patterns materialize, including lines radiating from the origin, and vague parabolic curves. Remember that if a solution like $(3, 4, 5)$ exists, then all integer multiples of this solution qualify as well. The angled lines in the plot are a result of this fact. The curves hint at an additional special relationship between a and b for certain integers. We will not delve into the details, but mathematicians can explain the relationship through well known formulas. The important observation is that integer solutions are readily available.

These integer solutions are another reason why the Pythagorean theorem is special. To see why, consider what happens if the algebra is slightly altered:

$$c^3 = a^3 + b^3$$

The powers are now 3 instead of 2. Are there any integer solutions to this equation? Solutions like $3, 4, 5$ no longer work because $3^3 + 4^3 = 91$, but $5^3 = 125$.

Powers of 4 could just as easily be substituted:

$$c^4 = a^4 + b^4$$

A bit of trial and error will show that integer solutions are not readily available.

In general, consider the equation:

$$c^n = a^n + b^n$$

where n is any integer. If $n = 4$ or $n = 3$ we get the previous equations, and if $n = 2$ we get the Pythagorean theorem.

There is a famous claim, first put forth by the French mathematician Pierre de Fermat over 350 years ago, that states:

No three positive integers satisfy the equation $c^n = a^n + b^n$ if n is greater than 2.

This is the world-renowned *Fermat's Last Theorem*, and it asserts that except for the special case of $n = 2$, no higher choice of power has integer solutions. The theorem gained notoriety after Fermat's death when this intriguing line was discovered in the margin of one of his books: "I have a truly marvelous demonstration of this proposition, which this margin is too narrow to contain."

Despite Fermat's tantalizing hint at a "marvelous" proof, his theorem beguiled mathematicians for centuries. Many great minds chipped away at it over the years, including the French mathematician Sophie Germain. Her impactful contributions toward solving the theorem in the early 19th century are particularly noteworthy considering the fact that she was self-taught. Not until the 1990s was a full proof finally submitted by the English mathematician Andrew Wiles.

Did Fermat really have an elegant proof of this theorem? It seems unlikely; after all, it stumped many of the greatest minds for hundreds of years. Wiles' proof employs some very advanced mathematics and required many years of dedicated work. The proof itself is over 100 pages long and took over a year for peer review. We may never know if Fermat really did discover a simpler version of the proof all those years ago.

The Pythagorean theorem remains one of the most recognizable equations of all time, and it has spawned countless applications in fields such as navigation, engineering, and surveying. The theorem also offers another example of a mathematical result that has far-reaching connections. It is baffling that although there are *infinitely* many integers to choose for the power n, and *infinitely* many integers to choose for a, b, and c, Fermat's Last Theorem says that none of them work if n is greater than 2. Clearly, there is something quite special about the Pythagorean Theorem beyond the simple geometry of right triangles.

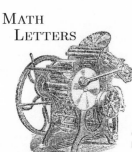

Sum of Squares & the Basel Problem

Letter 18

Mathematics knows no races or geographic boundaries; for mathematics, the cultural world is one country.
-David Hilbert

The power of mathematics stems from formulas that turn tedious tasks into simple calculations. One such formula, giving the sum of the first n integers, was presented in a previous letter:

$$1 + 2 + 3 + 4 + ... + n = \frac{n \cdot (n+1)}{2}$$

The formula above demonstrates how arduous calculations, like summing the first million integers, can be collapsed into a minor computation. Memorizing formulas is useful, but understanding their derivation offers much more insight. In fact, the main benefit of studying mathematics is the creative thinking process inherent in such derivations.

It is not always possible to find a compact formula for a given problem, and even when one does exist, there are usually many different ways to deduce it. The problem we will focus on today examines the sum of the first n *squared* integers:

$$1^2 + 2^2 + 3^2 + 4^2 + ... + n^2 = ?$$

For example, if $n = 4$ the sum comes out to:

$$1^2 + 2^2 + 3^2 + 4^2 = 1 + 4 + 9 + 16 = 30$$

There is a nice formula for the sum of squares, and a particularly interesting way to derive it.

To begin, recall that multiplication can be thought of as a convenient way to sum many copies of the same number. Adding three fives together is the same as $3 \cdot 5$. Likewise, $4 + 4 + 4 + 4$ is the same as $4 \cdot 4$ and so on. This implies that expressions like $4^2 = 4 \cdot 4$ and $5^2 = 5 \cdot 5$ can equivalently be written as $4 + 4 + 4 + 4$ and $5 + 5 + 5 + 5 + 5$.

Why is this meaningful? Well, it allows us to write square numbers using only addition. Here are the first five:

$$1^2 = 1 \cdot 1 = 1$$
$$2^2 = 2 \cdot 2 = 2 + 2$$
$$3^2 = 3 \cdot 3 = 3 + 3 + 3$$
$$4^2 = 4 \cdot 4 = 4 + 4 + 4 + 4$$
$$5^2 = 5 \cdot 5 = 5 + 5 + 5 + 5 + 5$$

To simplify the next step it is useful to focus on a small sample problem: a formula for the sum $1^2 + 2^2 + 3^2 + 4^2 + 5^2$. Restricting attention to a small concrete example and generalizing later is a useful problem-solving technique.

Every mathematical formula derivation requires at least one key flash of insight. It can take hours, days, years, or even centuries for someone to discover the insight; sometimes, no one has succeeded despite generations of effort, as evidenced by Goldbach's conjecture and the Collatz conjecture from previous letters. Luckily, the insight here is somewhat unexpected, but not overly complicated. The strategy is to write the sums above in the shape of a triangle:

$$\begin{array}{ccccccccc}
 & & & & 1 & & & & \\
 & & & 2 & & 2 & & & \\
 & & 3 & & 3 & & 3 & & \\
 & 4 & & 4 & & 4 & & 4 & \\
5 & & 5 & & 5 & & 5 & & 5
\end{array}$$

The rows of this triangle mimic the list of the first 5 squared integers using addition. The sum of the second row is 2^2, the sum of the third row is 3^2, and so on. If all the rows are summed together the output is $1^2 + 2^2 + 3^2 + 4^2 + 5^2$, which is exactly the sum we seek.

For the second step, notice that the triangle of numbers is equilateral, meaning that all sides have the same "length". Therefore, it can be rotated and maintain the same overall shape. The 3 possible rotations of this triangle are shown below. The first is just a copy of the one above. The next is a 120° clockwise rotation, and the last is an additional 120° clockwise rotation. The arrows illustrate the rotation required to attain the next triangle:

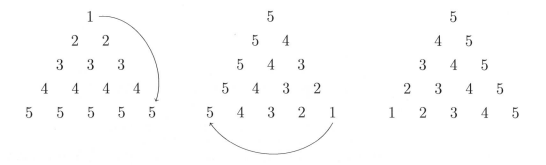

The numbers in each triangle are exactly the same; summing all the rows of any one still equals $1^2 + 2^2 + 3^2 + 4^2 + 5^2$.

148

Something rather unexpected happens when the entries of all 3 triangles are summed. The next triangle is formed by adding the respective entries of the other 3. For instance, the top number is the sum of the top entries $1 + 5 + 5$.

$$
\begin{array}{ccccccccc}
& & & & 11 & & & & \\
& & & 11 & & 11 & & & \\
& & 11 & & 11 & & 11 & & \\
& 11 & & 11 & & 11 & & 11 & \\
11 & & 11 & & 11 & & 11 & & 11
\end{array}
$$

Remarkably, every entry adds to 11, which can easily be verified by mentally checking each sum. The 11 in the bottom left corner is the result of the sum $5 + 5 + 1$, and the 11 in the middle is the sum $3 + 4 + 4$. The triangular rotations happen to align the numbers in just the right way to make each entry sum to the same number.

This is a significant discovery, but does a similar pattern hold for $1^2 + 2^2 + 3^2 + 4^2 + 5^2 + 6^2$? And more generally for $1^2 + 2^2 + 3^2 + 4^2 + ... + n^2$?

Adding another term to the sum simply adds another row onto the bottom of the triangle. The 3 rotated triangles for the sum $1^2 + 2^2 + 3^2 + 4^2 + 5^2 + 6^2$ are:

```
        1                        6                        6
      2   2                    6   5                    5   6
    3   3   3                6   5   4                4   5   6
  4   4   4   4            6   5   4   3            3   4   5   6
5   5   5   5   5        6   5   4   3   2        2   3   4   5   6
6 6 6 6 6 6            6 5 4 3 2 1            1 2 3 4 5 6
```

Adding up the numbers per position as we did before generates the triangle below:

$$
\begin{array}{cccccccccccc}
& & & & & 13 & & & & & \\
& & & & 13 & & 13 & & & & \\
& & & 13 & & 13 & & 13 & & & \\
& & 13 & & 13 & & 13 & & 13 & & \\
& 13 & & 13 & & 13 & & 13 & & 13 & \\
13 & & 13 & & 13 & & 13 & & 13 & & 13
\end{array}
$$

The final number is different, but the outcome of a single number still holds.

At this point, we can be fairly confident that the pattern is not a fluke. This is similar to the trick of finding a formula for the sum of the first n integers. In that case, the sum was written out twice and the numbers were rearranged, resulting in pairs that summed to the same number. The trick here is more sophisticated, but in essence, the sum is written out three times and arranged in an unexpected way.

How can this discovery be used to derive a formula? First of all, is there a formula for the single number in the final triangle? With the sum $1^2 + 2^2 + 3^2 + 4^2 + 5^2$ the final number was 11, and with the sum $1^2 + 2^2 + 3^2 + 4^2 + 5^2 + 6^2$ the final number was 13. Let's make an educated guess based on these two data points. One possibility is that the final number is $2 \cdot n + 1$, where n is the highest number in the sum. This works for the two cases thus far, $11 = 2 \cdot 5 + 1$ and $13 = 2 \cdot 6 + 1$.

To double check this guess we can write out the triangles for $1^2 + 2^2 + 3^2 + 4^2 + 5^2 + 6^2 + 7^2$. If the guess is correct, the final triangle should be filled with the number $2 \cdot 7 + 1 = 15$:

```
        1                             7                             7
      2   2                         7   6                         6   7
    3   3   3                     7   6   5                     5   6   7
  4   4   4   4                 7   6   5   4                 4   5   6   7
 5   5   5   5   5            7   6   5   4   3             3   4   5   6   7
6  6  6  6  6  6           7  6  5  4  3  2            2  3  4  5  6  7
7 7 7 7 7 7 7            7 6 5 4 3 2 1           1 2 3 4 5 6 7
```

Summing the entries yields:

```
                15
             15   15
          15   15   15
        15   15   15   15
      15   15   15   15   15
   15   15   15   15   15   15
 15   15   15   15   15   15   15
```

The result is 15 as predicted! Our initial guess of $2 \cdot n + 1$ for the final triangle is correct. If you need more convincing, look closely at the very top number of the triangle and note that it consists of the sum $1 + 7 + 7$, which is just another way of writing $2 \cdot 7 + 1$. Imagine writing out the corresponding 3 triangles for the general sum $1^2 + 2^2 + 3^2 + 4^2 + ... + n^2$. When they are summed to create the final triangle the top entry will always be $1 + n + n$, which is the same as $2 \cdot n + 1$.

The next question is: what is the sum of all numbers in the final triangle? This is not too difficult to work out because the numbers are all the same, and there is even a shortcut.

Consider the final 7 row triangle of 15s above. There is 1 copy of 15 in the first row, 2 copies in the second, 3 copies in the third, etc. The total number of 15s is $1 + 2 + 3 + 4 + 5 + 6 + 7$. We already have a formula for this! As mentioned earlier, the sum of the first n integers is given by the formula $\frac{n \cdot (n+1)}{2}$. In this case $n = 7$, so there are:

$$1 + 2 + 3 + 4 + 5 + 6 + 7 = \frac{7 \cdot (7+1)}{2} = 28$$

copies of the number 15.

It is not hard to see that the same pattern holds more generally. Looking back at the triangle of 13s there is 1 copy in the first row, 2 in the second, 3 in third and so on. The total number of 13s is $1+2+3+4+5+6$. This can also be verified for the triangle of 11s with $1+2+3+4+5$ copies appearing.

Bringing these two results together yields a formula for the sum of all the numbers in the final triangle. There will be $\frac{n \cdot (n+1)}{2}$ copies of the number $2 \cdot n + 1$; for instance, when $n = 7$ there were $\frac{7 \cdot (7+1)}{2} = 28$ copies of the number $2 \cdot 7 + 1 = 15$. This means that the sum of all copies of 15 in the final triangle will be $15 + 15 + 15 + ... + 15 = 420$, where 15 is written 28 times. A much easier way to write this is $28 \cdot 15 = 420$. In the general case, the sum of all numbers in the final triangle will be:

$$\left(\frac{n \cdot (n+1)}{2} \right) \cdot (2 \cdot n + 1)$$

The second term is the single number that makes up the final triangle, and the first term is the number of copies.

This formula can be verified using, for example, the previous triangle of 13s. In that scenario $n = 6$ and the sum of all numbers in the final triangle is:

$$\left(\frac{6 \cdot (6+1)}{2} \right) \cdot (2 \cdot 6 + 1) = 21 \cdot 13 = 273$$

Directly summing all copies of 13 in that triangle yields the same answer.

The final step is to think about what the sum of all numbers in the final triangle represents. Concretely, what does the above sum of 273 actually signify? It is the aggregate sum of numbers from *all 3 triangles*, meaning that 273 is three times the sum $1^2 + 2^2 + 3^2 + 4^2 + 5^2 + 6^2 = 91$. In other words:

$$273 = 3 \cdot (1^2 + 2^2 + 3^2 + 4^2 + 5^2 + 6^2)$$

If the formula for the sum of the final triangle is divided by 3 it will yield the sum we seek:

$$\frac{\left(\frac{n \cdot (n+1)}{2} \right) \cdot (2 \cdot n + 1)}{3}$$

This is the formula we have been searching for, and we can now write out the full result:

$$1^2 + 2^2 + 3^2 + 4^2 + ... + n^2 = \frac{\left(\frac{n \cdot (n+1)}{2} \right) \cdot (2 \cdot n + 1)}{3}$$

Let's test it with $n = 5$. Plugging 5 into the formula gives:

$$\frac{\left(\frac{5 \cdot (5+1)}{2} \right) \cdot (2 \cdot 5 + 1)}{3} = 55$$

which is the correct answer:
$$1^2 + 2^2 + 3^2 + 4^2 + 5^2 = 55$$

Let's try one more using $n = 6$:

$$\frac{\left(\frac{6 \cdot (6+1)}{2}\right) \cdot (2 \cdot 6 + 1)}{3} = 91$$

which is again the correct answer:

$$1^2 + 2^2 + 3^2 + 4^2 + 5^2 + 6^2 = 91$$

The formula breaks into 3 logical pieces. Using the example of $n = 6$ above, the first computations in the numerator consists of:

$$\frac{6 \cdot (6+1)}{2} = 21$$

and:

$$(2 \cdot 6 + 1) = 13$$

These two numbers represent the 21 copies of the number 13 in the final triangle, and multiplying them together gives the sum of all numbers in the final triangle:

$$21 \cdot 13 = 273$$

Since this is three times the answer to $1^2 + 2^2 + 3^2 + 4^2 + 5^2 + 6^2$, the last step is to divide by 3:

$$\frac{273}{3} = 91$$

Presented on its own, the formula for the sum of the first n squares appears mysterious, but behind every mathematical formula is a logical story. Great mathematicians are often able to recall complicated formulas by remembering key parts of their derivation. In this example, a mathematician may only need to associate the word "triangle" with the sum of squares problem to quickly remember the trick and derive the formula. This is a robust recall system, as deriving the formula from scratch eliminates the chance of misremembering it.

There is another interesting puzzle related to the sum of squares. Instead of summing up the square numbers themselves, what if we summed their *reciprocals*? The reciprocal of a number n is simply $\frac{1}{n}$, so the sum of square reciprocals is:

$$\frac{1}{1^2} + \frac{1}{2^2} + \frac{1}{3^2} + \frac{1}{4^2} + ... + \frac{1}{n^2}$$

On the surface, this looks similar to the problem we just solved, but it turns out that this one is much more difficult. Simply altering our formula by taking the reciprocal does not work—adding fractions is more complicated than summing integers.

Finding a formula for this sum is not trivial. In fact, a version of this problem was posed in the mid 17th century and sat unsolved for nearly 90 years. It asks for the infinite sum of square reciprocals:

$$\frac{1}{1^2} + \frac{1}{2^2} + \frac{1}{3^2} + \frac{1}{4^2} + \ldots = ?$$

Infinite sums were discussed in a previous letter on geometric series. Recall that infinite geometric series have the form:

$$x^1 + x^2 + x^3 + x^4 + \ldots$$

where x is a placeholder for any number between 0 and 1. In the aforementioned letter we proved the amazing result (replacing x with $\frac{1}{2}$):

$$\left(\frac{1}{2}\right)^1 + \left(\frac{1}{2}\right)^2 + \left(\frac{1}{2}\right)^3 + \left(\frac{1}{2}\right)^4 + \ldots = 2$$

Unfortunately, the sum of square reciprocals does not fit the definition of a geometric series. The powers stay fixed at 2 instead of increasing, and there is no single fixed fraction like $x = \frac{1}{2}$.

The infinite sum of square reciprocals is now known as the *Basel problem*—in honor of the Swiss mathematician's hometown who finally solved it. His name was Leonard Euler, and he was only 28 when he presented his solution in 1734. He is now well known as one of the greatest mathematicians of all time. The special number e is also named in his honor.

The problem has retained its fame over the years because the answer is so unexpected. Recall that geometrically, square numbers represent the area of a square. A circle is in some sense the opposite of a square because, unlike squares, circles contain no straight lines. Computing the area or circumference of a circle requires the irrational number π, and so π is intimately tied to circles, not squares. That is why it came as such a shock to the mathematical community when the answer to the Basel Problem was finally revealed:

$$\frac{1}{1^2} + \frac{1}{2^2} + \frac{1}{3^2} + \frac{1}{4^2} + \ldots = \frac{\pi^2}{6}$$

As covered in a previous letter on the concept of infinity and limits, the expression above says that the sum will eventually converge to the number $\frac{\pi^2}{6}$ as more terms are computed. It is astounding that π shows up in the answer; there is no reason to expect this when there are no curves or circles in sight, but rather, only reciprocals of square numbers!

The Basel problem is much more complicated than finding the formula for the sum of squared integers, but both problems require a good dose of imagination. Imagine trying to derive a formula for the sum of squared integers without knowing any of the tricks, like writing the squares using addition, or aligning the numbers in a triangle shape. Coming up with these ideas takes a great deal of creative trial and error. Nothing compares to the surge of satisfaction that comes from finally hitting upon an idea that solves the problem.

Measuring Infinity

Letter 19

Every good mathematician is at least half a philosopher, and every good philosopher is at least half a mathematician.
-Gottlob Frege

An earlier letter established the importance of infinity within mathematics and its usefulness for solving real-world problems through limits and calculus. Recall that infinity is not a number, but a concept, and the type of infinity encountered so far is known as *countable infinity*. However, this is not the only type of infinity—there is a more unusual kind which, in a sense, is even "bigger" than countable infinity.

How can one type of infinity be larger than another? To examine this concept, let's begin by exploring the usual notion of size for positive numbers. Given two numbers x and y, x is bigger than y if $x - y$ is positive. For instance, if $x = 100$ and $y = 10$, then $x - y = 100 - 10$ and the difference is 90; therefore, x is larger than y by exactly 90.

This works fine for numbers, but how does one measure the size of infinity? Infinity is not a number, so arithmetic like the subtraction of x and y above is useless. Measuring the size of an infinite quantity requires a new way of thinking and a more general notion of size.

Instead of relying on arithmetic, we will use a more basic idea, and it is best illustrated with a short example. Imagine 10 people standing around a table. In front of each person is a single empty chair. Are there as many people as there are chairs? This question can be answered rather easily without arithmetic—simply pair each person with each chair. If no chairs or people are left over then there must be as many people as there are chairs.

This concept of *pairing* is the key to measuring infinity, and in a way, it is even more fundamental than counting. Given two quantities, like chairs and people, all that is required is a way to pair an item from one category with an item from the other. In what follows, the quantities will be more abstract than people and chairs, but the underlying idea of pairing two sets of items together is the same.

The concept of infinity was introduced previously using the positive integers $1, 2, 3, 4, \ldots$. There are infinitely many positive integers, but what if these numbers are restricted to just the *even* positive integers $2, 4, 6, 8, \ldots$? Are there infinitely many even positive integers? The answer is yes, they go on forever just like the positive integers, but this leads to an interesting question: are there *more* positive integers than even positive integers?

To answer this, we will use the pairing idea to see if the set of all even integers can be paired with the set of all positive integers; the even integers represent the "people", and the positive integers represent the "chairs". There is only one problem—we have infinitely many items, and it is no longer possible to move through *every* pair. A slightly more sophisticated strategy is needed.

Instead of proceeding through every pair one by one, let's invent a *rule* to follow. A successful rule will pair off any item from one category with a unique item from the other. In this case, a very simple rule can be used:

Given an even positive integer n, its pair will be the positive integer $\frac{n}{2}$.

For example, the even integer 8 will be paired with the positive integer $\frac{8}{2} = 4$, and the even integer 2 will be paired with the positive integer $\frac{2}{2} = 1$. The pairing of the first several even integers appears below. The trailing vertical dots at the end signify that the list goes on forever.

$$2 \to 1$$
$$4 \to 2$$
$$6 \to 3$$
$$8 \to 4$$
$$10 \to 5$$
$$12 \to 6$$
$$14 \to 7$$
$$\vdots \to \vdots$$

The rule of dividing by 2 helps us travel from the even integers in the left column to the positive integers in the right column. Of course, the columns technically go on forever, but the point is that the rule can map *any* even integer to a *unique* corresponding positive integer.

Rules like the one above allow a notion of "size" to be assigned to infinity, and it brings us to the definition of countable infinity: An infinite set of numbers is *countably infinite* if each number can be paired with a unique positive integer. The term *set* has a precise meaning in mathematics, but for our purposes, a set is just a group of numbers. Counting how many numbers are contained in a *finite* set is easy. There are 5 numbers in the set $1, 3, 6, 8, 9$. However, when counting sets of infinite size a different method for measuring "how many" numbers there are is required.

According to the definition of countable infinity, the set of all even integers is countably infinite, because dividing by 2 successfully pairs every even integer with a unique positive integer.

How about the odd integers $1, 3, 5, 7, ...$? These are also countably infinite, and the rule is similar to the one used to pair off the even integers. To pair each odd integer with a unique positive integer the rule is:

Given an odd positive integer n, its pair will be the positive integer $\frac{n+1}{2}$.

For instance, 1 will be mapped to itself $\frac{1+1}{2} = 1$ and 3 will be mapped to $\frac{3+1}{2} = 2$. The pairing of the first several odd integers appears below:

$$1 \to 1$$
$$3 \to 2$$
$$5 \to 3$$
$$7 \to 4$$
$$9 \to 5$$
$$11 \to 6$$
$$13 \to 7$$
$$\vdots \to \vdots$$

Again, this pairing goes on forever. Just as with the even integers, the rule allows us to map any odd integer to a unique positive integer.

Let's look at one last example. Is the set of square numbers $1, 4, 9, 16, \ldots$ countably infinite? The answer is yes, and the rule to pair them with the positive integers is:

Given a square integer n, its pair will be the positive integer $\sqrt{n}$.

The pairing of the first several square numbers looks like this:

$$1 \to 1$$
$$4 \to 2$$
$$9 \to 3$$
$$16 \to 4$$
$$25 \to 5$$
$$36 \to 6$$
$$49 \to 7$$
$$\vdots \to \vdots$$

The examples above lead to a somewhat unintuitive conclusion. The "size" of the set of all positive integers is the same "size" as the set of all even integers, all odd integers, and all square numbers. This result conflicts with our intuitive understanding of size, because it seems like there should be more positive integers than any of the aforementioned sets. After all, the positive integers contain all the even *and* all the odd integers. However, when dealing with infinite quantities our standard notion of size does not apply; what matters is the *type* of infinity, and these sets of numbers are all countably infinite.

Countable infinity is the most common type of infinity utilized within mathematics. Incredibly, there exists an even "bigger" type of infinity. To uncover it, let's move to other sets of numbers beyond the integers.

The *rational* numbers consist of all integer ratios. Standard fractions like $\frac{1}{2}$, $\frac{7}{10}$, $\frac{11}{5}$ are all rational. The positive integers, in fact, are a subset of the rational numbers because each can trivially be written as itself over 1.

Now consider the set of all positive rational numbers. The size of this set is infinite because it contains all the positive integers as a subset, but it contains many other numbers as well. Consider the sequence $\frac{1}{1}, \frac{1}{2}, \frac{1}{3}, \frac{1}{4}, \ldots$ These fractions go on forever, and they are all rational numbers. Changing the numerator to any other integer, say 2, produces another infinite sequence of rational numbers $\frac{2}{1}, \frac{2}{2}, \frac{2}{3}, \frac{2}{4}, \ldots$. There may be some repetition (like $\frac{1}{2} = \frac{2}{4}$), but infinitely many infinite sequences of rational numbers can be produced. In summary, the "size" of the set of all positive rational numbers certainly seems like a good candidate to *not* be countably infinite.

To determine whether the set of all positive rational numbers is countably infinite they need to be paired off with the positive integers. The challenge is developing a methodology to organize the rational numbers in the first place. Luckily, a strategy developed by the German mathematician Georg Cantor in the late 19th century can help. Cantor was the first to rigorously establish the existence of different types of infinity, and he developed a scheme to visualize the pairing of the positive rationals with the positive integers.

The trick is to imagine an infinite grid containing all the positive rational numbers. The dots appearing along the right and bottom edge signify the infinite continuation of the grid:

$$
\begin{array}{cccccc}
\frac{1}{1} & \frac{1}{2} & \frac{1}{3} & \frac{1}{4} & \frac{1}{5} & \cdots \\[2mm]
\frac{2}{1} & \frac{2}{2} & \frac{2}{3} & \frac{2}{4} & \frac{2}{5} & \cdots \\[2mm]
\frac{3}{1} & \frac{3}{2} & \frac{3}{3} & \frac{3}{4} & \frac{3}{5} & \cdots \\[2mm]
\frac{4}{1} & \frac{4}{2} & \frac{4}{3} & \frac{4}{4} & \frac{4}{5} & \cdots \\[2mm]
\frac{5}{1} & \frac{5}{2} & \frac{5}{3} & \frac{5}{4} & \frac{5}{5} & \cdots \\[2mm]
\vdots & \vdots & \vdots & \vdots & \vdots & \cdots
\end{array}
$$

The numerator is constant across each row and the denominator increases by 1 from column to column. Every positive rational number appears somewhere in this grid. There is even a simple system to find an arbitrary rational number $\frac{x}{y}$: it will be located in row x and column y. For instance, $\frac{4}{3}$ can be found in the 4th row and 3rd column.

Creating a strategy to organize all the rational numbers is half the battle; now we need a way to pair them up with the positive integers. Unfortunately, a rigorous proof of this pairing is complicated. Instead, we will illustrate a heuristic argument presented by Georg Cantor himself.

The key is to form a zig-zag pattern through each rational in the grid. The arrows indicate the direction of travel.

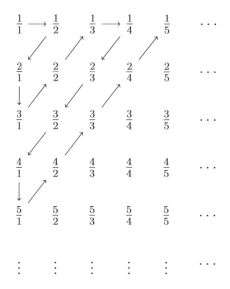

The very first rational $\frac{1}{1}$ at the start of the path will be paired with 1, then $\frac{1}{2}$ will be paired with 2, and $\frac{2}{1}$ with 3, and so on. If the zig-zag path crosses a rational number that has already been paired (e.g. $\frac{1}{2} = \frac{2}{4}$) then it is simply skipped.

It turns out that the positive rational numbers *are* countably infinite. The rule described above is admittedly nothing more than a visual heuristic, but a list based on the path would look like the one below. Notice that if a number has already been accounted for then it is skipped:

$$\frac{1}{1} \rightarrow 1$$

$$\frac{1}{2} \rightarrow 2$$

$$\frac{2}{1} \rightarrow 3$$

$$\frac{3}{1} \rightarrow 4$$

$$\frac{1}{3} \rightarrow 5$$

$$\frac{1}{4} \rightarrow 6$$

$$\vdots \rightarrow \vdots$$

The "size" of the set of positive rational numbers is the same "size" as the positive integers. On the surface, this assertion seems absurd, but remember how the concept of size is being used. Both the positive rational numbers and the positive integers are countably infinite, which means they can be paired together in a never-ending list.

The crux of Cantor's proof rests on the certainty that every rational number appears somewhere in the grid above. As the path weaves through it will cross every positive rational number $\frac{x}{y}$ when it reaches row x and column y. The fact that the rational numbers can be nicely organized in the first place is what differentiates countable infinity from the more bizarre kind of infinity we will turn to next.

The *real* numbers are made up of all the rational numbers together with all the irrational numbers. Recall that irrational numbers are the rather strange quantities like $\pi = 3.14159...$ and $\sqrt{2} = 1.4142...$ where the decimal representation goes on forever with no discernible repeating pattern. The real numbers encompass our entire familiar number system, but let's focus on a particular segment—all real numbers between 0 and 1.

Is the set of all real numbers between 0 and 1 countably infinite? The only way to find out is to try to pair them with the positive integers; however, it is not clear where to begin. The even, odd, and square numbers were easy to organize and list. For the rational numbers, there was a slightly more sophisticated technique that relied on a grid. In this scenario, the real numbers between 0 and 1 all have the form $.xxxxxxxx...$ where each x can be replaced with an integer (e.g. $.1435276...$, $.33333...$, or $.9000...$). While some real numbers have a decimal representation that continues forever, others have a repeating or finite representation. There is no obvious way to arrange these numbers.

For the sake of argument let's assume that we *can* list out all the numbers between 0 and 1. Using random real numbers and pairing them with the positive integers might look like this:

$$.123567... \rightarrow 1$$
$$.258790... \rightarrow 2$$
$$.012987... \rightarrow 3$$
$$.890981... \rightarrow 4$$
$$.997632... \rightarrow 5$$
$$.542386... \rightarrow 6$$
$$\vdots \rightarrow \vdots$$

There is no well-defined strategy here; the point is to visualize an *attempt* to pair up the real numbers between 0 and 1 with the positive integers.

The incredible truth is that it is not possible to list out all numbers between 0 and 1 in this manner—the type of infinity is different. The set of all numbers between 0 and 1 is *uncountably infinite*, and is even "bigger" than countable infinity. It is an infinity so large that it cannot be matched up with the positive integers.

The proof demonstrating this amazing property starts by assuming that the real numbers between 0 and 1 *are* countably infinite, and proceeds to show that this assumption cannot possibly be true (i.e. a proof by contradiction). This is achieved by fabricating a real number that is missing from *any* purported mapping of the real numbers to the positive integers.

To see this argument in action, suppose a rule was developed that yielded the example list above. Although this list uses arbitrary real numbers, any scheme attempting to pair the real numbers with the positive integers would work. The goal is to use this example mapping to show that any such pairing would be missing at least one real number, therefore invalidating it.

To this end, take the mapping above and consider the first digit of the first number, the second digit of the second number, the third digit of the third number and so on. These digits are underlined below:

.<u>1</u>23567...

.2<u>5</u>8790...

.01<u>2</u>987...

.890<u>9</u>81...

.9976<u>3</u>2...

.54238<u>6</u>...

$$\vdots$$

We will form a new decimal number between 0 and 1 using these underlined digits. If they are lined up in decimal format the first six digits will be .152936.... Next, each digit will be altered by adding 1, and if the digit is a 9 it will be changed to 0. This produces the new number:

.263047...

which consists of the underlined digits above, each incremented by 1. This is just the start of the new number; we can continue down the list forever, in the nth row take the nth digit, add 1 to it, and append it to the new number above.

This is the magic number that invalidates the list! It is a real number between 0 and 1, but it cannot possibly be in the infinite list. To see why, suppose someone disagrees and claims that the number above *is* in the list. If this is true, then ask which row it is in. For the sake of argument assume they declare that it appears in row 100. Take the number in row 100 and find the digit in the 100th decimal place. Then find the digit in the 100th decimal place of the new number above and compare. By construction, the digits in the 100th decimal place will differ by 1, so the two numbers cannot be the same. No matter which row the number is claimed to appear in, say row n, we can always show that the new number differs by 1 in the nth decimal place.

Another way to see this is to imagine traveling down the proposed list and comparing each number to the new number. The new number cannot be the first number .123567... in the list—the digit in the first decimal place is 1 while the digit in the first decimal place of the new number is 2. It cannot be the second number .258790... in the list—the digit in the second decimal place is 5 while the digit in the second decimal place of the new number is 6. In this manner, imagine scrolling down the entire infinite list to show that the new number must be different from every other. Therefore, the pairing must be incomplete due to the absence of this number.

Admittedly, this argument is a bit mind-bending, so it helps to think back to the grid of rational numbers. In that case, an argument like the one above would not be possible. Any claim that the grid was missing a particular rational number $\frac{x}{y}$ could immediately be disproved by pointing to row x and column y. The difference with the real numbers is that regardless of the proposed pairing with the positive integers, it is always possible to use this scheme to create a new number that is missing from the list. The real numbers cannot be paired with the positive integers—there are simply "too many" of them.

One dramatic way to state these results is to claim that there are "more" numbers crowded between 0 and 1 than there are positive integers or even positive rational numbers. We focused on the real numbers between 0 and 1 for ease of illustration, but the same argument can be applied to any interval of real numbers.

This gives rise to another curious takeaway: irrational numbers must be the culprits behind the uncountability property. The real numbers are made up of the rational numbers together with the irrational numbers. If the rationals are countably infinite, but the rationals together with the irrationals are uncountably infinite, then the irrationals must be causing the difference. This is yet another reason why the irrational numbers are so strange. There are a lot "more" of them than there are rationals.

The notion that different types of infinity exist verges on the philosophical, and through the years it has led to many impassioned arguments between mathematicians. One question of particular renown, posed by Georg Cantor in 1878, has come to be known as the *continuum hypothesis*. It asks: is there a type of infinity *between* countable and uncountable infinity? Namely, can one construct an infinite set of numbers that is too large to pair with the positive integers, but too small to pair with the real numbers? Cantor asserted that the answer is no, but was unable to prove it. This remains one of the most important unsettled questions in theoretical mathematics. The allure of studying such problems is that bewildering new ideas can be demonstrated using nothing more than pencil and paper.

Fractals with Complex Numbers
Letter 20

The study of mathematics, like the Nile, begins in minuteness but ends in magnificence.
-Charles Caleb Colton

Fractal images are one of the most beautiful discoveries to emerge from the long-running partnership between mathematics and computer science. Although the images contain complicated geometric detail, they are usually the end result of relatively simple rules applied repeatedly. As demonstrated in earlier letters, the methods for drawing them are not nearly as complicated as the images themselves.

Before proceeding to our main subject, one new concept must be introduced—*complex numbers*. For our purposes, complex numbers will be viewed as nothing more than a tool to draw fractals, and we will restrict our attention to a few key concepts.

To begin, consider a right triangle with two sides of length 1 and an unknown third side of length x:

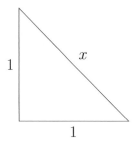

By the Pythagorean theorem x must satisfy:

$$x^2 = 1^2 + 1^2$$

and so the unknown side length must solve $x^2 = 2$. Mathematicians had to invent a symbol, the square root, to represent the solution $x = \sqrt{2} = 1.41421....$ As discussed in an earlier letter, $\sqrt{2}$ is an irrational number.

Equations like $x^2 = c$, where c is some number, arise frequently in mathematics. It was only a matter of time until someone came across the equation $x^2 = -1$. Is there a solution to this equation? Unfortunately, none of our familiar numbers work. When a number is squared (even a negative number) the result is always positive.

Mathematicians were left no choice but to invent another symbol, and the one they came up with was i. It is defined as $i = \sqrt{-1}$. Squaring i yields:

$$i^2 = -1$$

Therefore, $x = i$ is a solution to the equation $x^2 = -1$. This is analogous to the invention of the square root symbol. Taking square roots of real numbers helped lead to the discovery of a new set of numbers—the irrational numbers. Likewise, i led to the discovery of a new class of numbers—the complex numbers.

This vastly oversimplifies both the discovery and usage of i, but the basic idea is that i can be used to spawn a new set of numbers. There are actually many real-world problems in fields such as electrical engineering that make heavy use of i; it is not an arbitrary mathematical invention.

Our interest in i lies solely in its use as a tool to draw fractals. Known as the *imaginary unit*, the symbol i is somewhat similar to the positive integer 1. Just as 1 can be multiplied by other numbers to scale it up and down, i can likewise be multiplied by other real numbers to scale it up and down. For instance, $5 \cdot i$, $2.3 \cdot i$, and $-7.3 \cdot i$ are all valid operations. It is traditional to omit the multiplication dot and just write $5i$, $2.3i$, and $-7.3i$ for these numbers.

Numbers like $5i$ are used to solve equations such as $x^2 = -25$. Besides multiplying i by real numbers, we can also add and subtract real numbers like $2 + 3i$, $1.5 - 3.2i$, and $.3 + .5i$. Any number of the form $a + bi$ where a and b are real numbers and i is the imaginary unit is called a *complex number*.

Complex numbers can be viewed as an extension of our familiar real number system, and they are produced by multiplying and adding real numbers to i. Just as the real numbers can be visualized on an infinite straight line, the complex numbers can be visualized on an infinite two-dimensional plane. The horizontal axis contains all real numbers and the vertical axis contains all multiples of the imaginary unit i. Here is the complex plane with three example complex numbers highlighted:

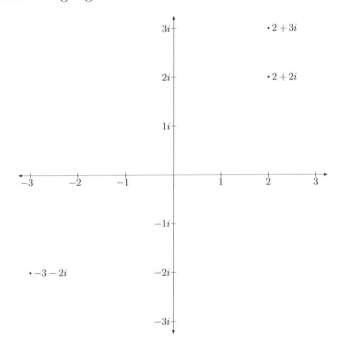

The complex plane acts like a blank canvas. Each point represents a single complex number, and schemes can be developed to shade in certain groups of numbers.

There is one last item to address before moving on to fractals; arithmetic with complex numbers. Remember, we are using complex numbers as nothing more than a tool to draw fractals, so the following rules can be thought of as an instruction manual for proper use.

Addition of complex numbers is straightforward. Add the real parts together and then add the imaginary parts together:

$$(2 + 3i) + (1 + 5i) = (3 + 8i)$$

In other words, complex addition is just like regular addition except that it is done twice; once for the real parts and once for the imaginary parts.

Complex multiplication relies on the distributive property of regular multiplication. In fact, it is just an application of the FOIL method often taught in middle school. As a reminder, FOIL is an acronym for First, Outer, Inner, Last, and is an easy way to remember the order of multiplication for quantities like $(a + b) \cdot (c + d)$:

$$(a + b) \cdot (c + d) = a \cdot c + a \cdot d + b \cdot c + b \cdot d$$

The FOIL method works just the same when two complex numbers are multiplied together. For instance, to multiply $(2 + 3i)$ and $(1 + 5i)$ simply plug in $a = 2, b = 3i, c = 1$, and $d = 5i$ to get:

$$(2 + 3i) \cdot (1 + 5i) = 2 \cdot 1 + 2 \cdot 5i + 3i \cdot 1 + 3i \cdot 5i$$

Everything on the right can be multiplied and summed as normal, with the exception of the $3i \cdot 5i$ term. There are two i terms multiplied together, which results in an i^2 term. Remember that $i = \sqrt{-1}$ so that $i^2 = -1$. Substituting -1 for i^2 yields $3i \cdot 5i = 15i^2 = -15$. The remaining multiplication and addition on the right side can now be completed:

$$\begin{aligned} (2 + 3i) \cdot (1 + 5i) &= 2 \cdot 1 + 2 \cdot 5i + 3i \cdot 1 + 3i \cdot 5i \\ &= 2 + 10i + 3i - 15 \\ &= (-13 + 13i) \end{aligned}$$

Complex multiplication is slightly more involved than regular multiplication, but there are logical rules to follow just as there are for real numbers.

Taken together, complex addition, multiplication, and the complex plane can be used to paint fractals. The "brush" will be the simple mathematical function below:

$$x^2 + c$$

The inputs will be complex numbers. Complex multiplication will be used to compute the x^2 term, and complex addition will be used to add the c term.

Notice that the function actually has *two* inputs, x and c. To obtain a function with only one input let's fix the c term to a specific number, like $c = .5 + .25i$, and work with the resulting function:

$$x^2 + (.5 + .25i)$$

This function will be used to create a *feedback loop*—akin to the ones in our previous letter on chaos and feedback loops. The only difference is that we are now using complex numbers.

For the sake of illustration, let's use the example function above to create a feedback loop starting with the arbitrary initial input $1 + .1i$. Plugging this in for x gives:

$$(1 + .1i)^2 + (.5 + .25i) = 1.49 + .45i$$

To continue the feedback loop we will take the output of $1.49 + .45i$ and feed it into the function $x^2 + (.5 + .25i)$ once again:

$$(1.49 + .45i)^2 + (.5 + .25i) = 2.5176 + 1.591i$$

The first three numbers of the feedback loop are therefore:

$$(1 + .1i), (1.49 + .45i), (2.5176 + 1.591i)$$

The parentheses around each complex number are only meant to make the list more legible.

The methodology above should look familiar; this process can continue indefinitely, because the last output can always act as the next input. Instead of generating a sequence of real numbers, as in the aforementioned letter on chaos and feedback loops, we are generating a sequence of complex numbers.

A sequence of real numbers can be visualized as a progression of points on a number line. For example, the sequence .5, 2.3, 2.8 starts at .5, jumps to 2.3, and then jumps to 2.8:

As the picture demonstrates, visualizing sequences of real numbers is not very interesting—they are only points on a line. Complex numbers, however, can be visualized in a two-dimensional plane. Consider the start of the feedback loop:

$$(1 + .1i), (1.49 + .45i), (2.5176 + 1.591i)$$

The real part, or first term, of each number corresponds to the horizontal real axis, and the imaginary part, or second term, corresponds to the vertical imaginary axis. The point $2.5176 + 1.591i$ is found by tracing over to 2.5176 on the real axis and up to 1.591i on the imaginary axis.

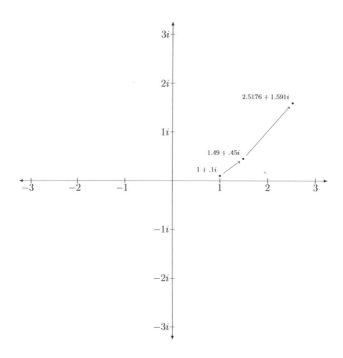

Based on the visual above, sequences of complex numbers created by a feedback loop "move around" the plane. Some sequences will continue to grow and move away from the origin, while others may settle down near a single point. Other sequences may eventually oscillate between several points.

We are finally ready to explore the peculiar properties of feedback loops generated by $x^2 + c$. The first step is to choose a complex number c and obtain a function with one input, which for the first drawing will be $c = 0$. This yields the function:

$$x^2$$

This function can be used to create an image on the complex plane.

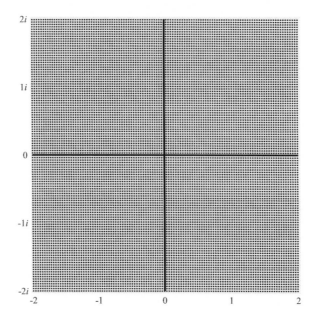

Grid of Points in the Complex Plane

Each point in the grid above corresponds to a complex number, and the two crossing bold lines represent the real and imaginary axes just as before (the labels have been moved to the margins). This square plane contains all complex numbers with real and imaginary parts between -2 and 2. It would be too tedious to label every point, but the value of any point can be inferred by noting its location using the real and imaginary axes. The point in the very upper left corner is the number $-2 + 2i$, and the point in the very upper right corner is the number $2 + 2i$.

The next step is to move through this grid point by point and erase some of them using the function x^2. Each point will act as the initial input to create a feedback loop, and as the loop progresses it will create a sequence of complex numbers that "move around" the plane. If at any time during the feedback loop the point leaves the square grid we've drawn, then the initial point will be erased.

If, for example, we test the point $1 - 2i$, the first few terms of the feedback loop generated by x^2 are:
$$(1 - 2i), (-3 - 4i), (-7 + 24i), \dots$$
To remain within the square the real and imaginary parts must both be between -2 and 2; therefore, by the second term $-3 - 4i$ we have already moved outside of the square. This indicates that the initial point $1 - 2i$ should be erased.

What about the point $.3 + .2i$? Using this as the initial input for the feedback loop generated by x^2 produces:
$$(.3 + .2i), (.05 + .12i), (-.0119 + .012i), \dots$$
As the feedback loop progresses, the real and imaginary parts shrink toward 0. It turns out that this sequence of points never leaves the square and the numbers just "move" toward the origin. This is an example of a point to keep, so $.3 + .2i$ is not erased and remains on the grid.

In this manner, we can move across every point in the grid and decide whether it should be kept or erased. The end result is the image below:

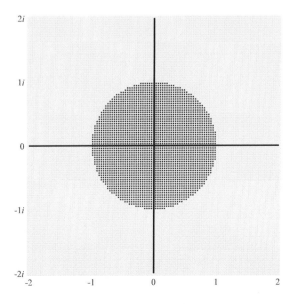

Using x^2 Feedback Loop to Erase Points

A circle of radius 1 emerges—and after a bit of thought, this makes sense. The function x^2 works on complex and real numbers in a similar way; for real numbers, the feedback loop created by x^2 diverges off to infinity outside of the interval -1 to 1, and converges to 0 for all numbers between -1 and 1. This property translates to the complex numbers, but instead of ending with a one-dimensional interval from -1 to 1, there is a two-dimensional circle with radius 1. All the points within the circle converge toward 0 and never leave the square, while all the points outside the circle diverge off to infinity.

Although the emergence of a circle is interesting, the key to generating truly astounding images lies in choosing special values for c. The exercise above is repeated below using various values of c, and each one generates a different final image.

Let's try $c = -.7269 + .1889i$. This yields the function:

$$x^2 + (-.7269 + .1889i)$$

After stepping through the grid point by point and testing each one using the new function $x^2 + (-.7269 + .1889i)$, the resulting image is:

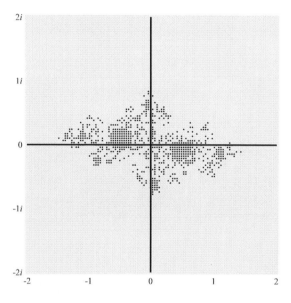

Using $x^2 + (-.7269 + .1889i)$ Feedback Loop to Erase Points

This certainly isn't a circle, but the image is rather coarse. The problem is that the density of points is too low to reveal much detail. The starting grid of points was fine for demonstration purposes, but boosting the resolution requires increasing the number of points and decreasing their size.

The original grid contained roughly 13000 points; the following image increases this to nearly one million, and the point size is significantly reduced.

The higher resolution image appears next.

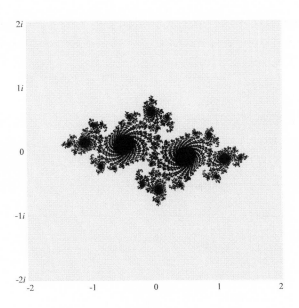

Using $x^2 + (-.7269 + .1889i)$ Feedback Loop to Erase Points

This is an absolutely stunning image! The higher resolution makes a huge difference. Note the subtle symmetry and fascinating self-similarity. It is amazing that the change from $c = 0$ to $c = -.7269 + .1889i$ produces such a wildly different outcome.

Are there other values of c that produce intricate images? The following are renderings using the same methodology, but different values for c.

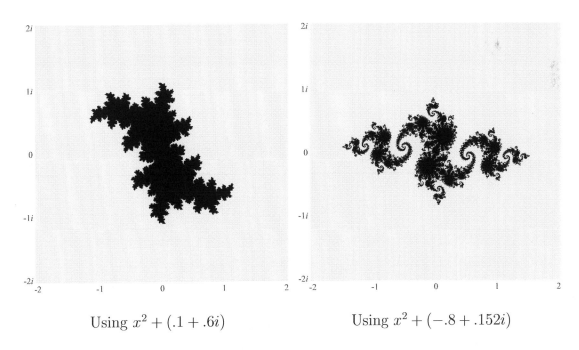

Using $x^2 + (.1 + .6i)$　　　　　　　Using $x^2 + (-.8 + .152i)$

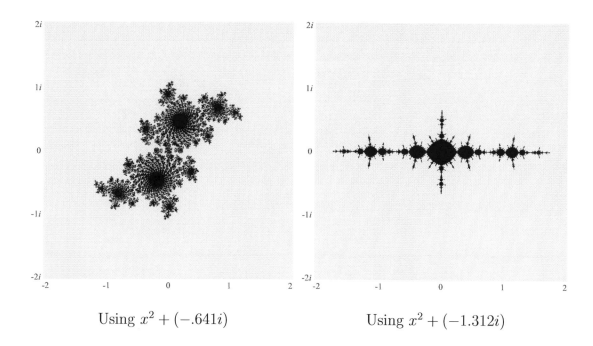

Using $x^2 + (-.641i)$ Using $x^2 + (-1.312i)$

These images are truly spectacular, and this is only a sampling of the possibilities. Collectively, these plots of points are known as *Julia sets*, after the French mathematician Gaston Julia who discovered them in the early 20th century.

The uniqueness of fractals stems from the fact that we can, at least theoretically, zoom in forever without losing detail. The images thus far are remarkable, but of course, the detail of any image is limited by the size of pixels on a screen or ink droplets on a page.

Nonetheless, we can perform some magnification. The next picture zooms into the image produced by the function $x^2 + (-.641i)$. Note the coordinate labels on the left and bottom edges. This is the portion of the complex plane with real and imaginary parts between $-.25$ and $.25$.

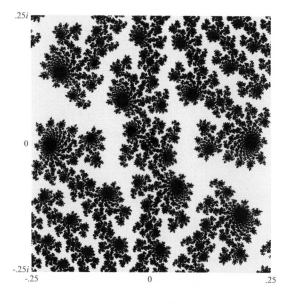

Zoomed Image of $x^2 + (-.641i)$

The smaller floral shapes bear a certain resemblance to the overall picture, and if the zooming continues, each of these smaller patterns will contain similar sub-patterns.

One more zoomed image appears next. This one focuses on a pair of spiral arms produced by the function $x^2 + (-.8 + .152i)$. The zoom region contains the area of the image between .25 and .75 on the real axis and $-.25i$ and $.25i$ on the imaginary axis:

Zoomed Image of $x^2 + (-.8 + .152i)$

As in our previous letter on fractals, many of the shapes above seem to have an almost "organic" appearance. Comparable patterns can be found in diverse natural phenomena like snowflakes, clouds, crystals, coastlines, and seashells to name a few. This is one of the primary drivers behind scientists' interest in fractals and their formation. They seem to suggest that the intricate designs of nature may be governed by delicate mathematical rules.

Index

Made in the USA
Las Vegas, NV
05 November 2023

80233212R00106